I AM CANADA

SNIPER FIRE

The Fight for Ortona

Jonathan Webb

Scholastic Canada Ltd.
Toronto New York London Auckland Sydney
Mexico City New Delhi Hong Kong Buenos Aires

While the events described and some of the characters in this book may be based on actual historical events and real people, Paul Baldassara is a fictional character created by the author, and his story is a work of fiction.

A Dear Canada Book. Published by Scholastic Canada Ltd.
SCHOLASTIC and I AM CANADA and logos are trademarks and/or registered trademarks of Scholastic Inc.

www.scholastic.ca

Library and Archives Canada Cataloguing in Publication

Webb, Jonathan, 1950-, author
Sniper fire : the fight for Ortona / Jonathan Webb.
(I am Canada)
Issued in print and electronic formats.
ISBN 978-1-4431-2861-2 (hardcover).--ISBN 978-1-4431-4681-4 (html)
1. Ortona, Battle of, Ortona, Italy, 1943--Juvenile fiction.
I. Title. II. Series: I am Canada
PS8595.E22S65 2016 jC813'.54 C2016-900930-0
C2016-900931-9

6 5 4 3 2 1 Printed in Canada 114 16 17 18 19 20

The display type was set in Happy Daze.
The text was set in Minion.

First printing September 2016

For Vivian

Chapter 1
Colle d'Anchise
October 23, 1943

"The Jerries are up there," says the Gaffer, pointing.

"Up where?" says Derrick O'Connor. "All I see is fog."

"You've got your eyes closed then, you idiot," says Paddy. "There's nothing but fog in that head of yours."

The Gaffer ignores them, like he usually does when the brothers are bickering. "There's at least a couple of companies of Grenadiers on the mountain," he says. "They've turfed the civilians out of a village and taken over their houses. That's what G2 says anyway. The village is called Colle d'Anchise."

"What?" says Derrick.

"Collie Dank-he-say," says Doug. Doug's been studying Italian.

"That doesn't sound right to me," says Danny. "How do you say it, Baldassara?"

"I dunno," I say. "It's not how my ma would say it. But maybe it's close enough."

Danny never calls me by my first name, which is Paul, though my ma still calls me Paolo. Danny thinks my last name is funny. I pretend to have trouble saying his. It's Polish: Kurlowitz. Curl-o-wuv-itch.

"Put a sock in it, boys," says Strong John Stonechild. Strong John doesn't talk much and sometimes he likes it best when we don't talk either. But this time Doug, who likes to talk, supports him.

"He's right," he says. "Sound carries over water."

"Aw, they probably know we're here," says Derrick. But he shuts up just the same.

We keep legging it up the hill, in the dark, with the mist wrapped around our heads, while the Biferno River splashes beside us. Somewhere below us a squadron of tanks from the Ontario Regiment has been mobilized to support us, but our battalion of Edmonton riflemen is spearheading the attack. Lieutenant Gold says it will be a piece of cake. The Gaffer, who doesn't believe there's any such thing as a piece of cake, says nothing.

It's not much of a river, the Biferno. Just another in a series of streams that rolls down from the mountains in a winding path to the Adriatic Sea. Maybe it's deeper when it gets to the end. We crossed it yesterday, just waded in, barely got our butts wet. Of course, it's not like the army gave us waterproof boots, so last night we had to wring out our socks and dig in our packs for dry ones.

"What's your single most important piece of equipment, Baldassara?"

This is one of the Gaffer's favourite questions. There are plenty of answers. One of them is rude. You can never be sure what the right answer is because it changes depending on the Gaffer's mood. This time I guess right.

"Dry socks, Sergeant."

It sounds like a joke, but it's awful what happens if you don't take care of your feet. The skin turns black and falls away like the leaves from a rancid cabbage. Smells like bad cabbage too. Some of the guys use army-issue foot powder. I just try to keep my feet dry. Like Danny once said, we can defeat the Germans if the army doesn't de-feet us first.

* * *

We crossed over from Sicily to the mainland back in September. We had it pretty easy for the first month or so. It seemed like the enemy was disorganized. The Italian dictator, Mussolini, who used to be Hitler's buddy, was kicked out. Another government was formed and it was supposed to come over to the Allied side, but in the meantime a large part of the Italian army surrendered. In fact, most of the Italian soldiers we saw were so eager to stop fighting that they met us on the beach, threw down their rifles and helped us unload the landing craft. They pointed in the direction where they said the Germans had gone. They couldn't have been more helpful. It was kind of embarrassing, to tell you the truth, to see soldiers from my parents' home country in such a hurry to give up. What the other guys had to say about them was brutal. They called them cowards and worse. Much worse. I kept my mouth shut. But I was glad the Italian soldiers were surrendering too. I mean, I was ready to kill them when they were the enemy. That's what I'd been trained to do. It's what I signed up for. But now I didn't have to.

We didn't see the Germans for a while. We saw their planes, the Luftwaffe. Sometimes we were strafed by them. Mostly what we saw was the destruction they left behind as they pulled back from the toe of the Italian boot, where we landed, to the middle. Sometimes we ran into German demolition parties. They blew up bridges and busted up roads as they retreated, anything to slow us down. I think they also wanted to punish the Italians for deserting them, by making their lives miserable. If that was their plan, they did a good job.

We had a few scraps in the first few weeks and sometimes we got shelled. And then things got bad. The Germans would set up a defensive position on high ground or behind a river. They would establish fields of fire with their machine guns aimed at us in overlapping arcs. They would dig bunkers to conceal their big guns. When we advanced, they would lob mortar fire at us, and cut us up with their heavy machine guns. We took a bunch of casualties.

The truth is that we lost as many men to sickness as we did to the Germans. We were told not to pick fruit from farmers' orchards or vegetables from their fields. Yeah, right! Never mind the juicy peaches, boys: dig into this army slop instead! Some guys got the runs so bad from eating dirty fruit, they had to be pulled out of the line. And it wasn't just diarrhea that thinned out our ranks. Soldiers turned yellow and weak from jaundice and had to be sent back. Others caught malaria, which made them see things that weren't there. They got sent behind the line to get better too.

On the other side of the mountains, working their way up the western side of the boot, the Americans are closing in on Rome. On our side, the eastern side, we're part of the British Eighth Army commanded by General Montgomery, and our objective, as far as I know, is to keep going, to keep pushing the Germans back to where they came from. One river and mountain-top village at a time.

* * *

We climb the last stretch of mountain in silence. The mist is getting thinner and the sun is beginning to show itself when we halt behind an outbuilding near the summit. It's so quiet: not a horse whinnies or rooster crows. There's nothing to suggest that a sentry has been posted, no sound of a match being struck or of stamping feet. I can make out Danny's lean face now, as he peers around the shed. The sun lights a spark in his dark eyes.

"They're not ready for us," he says softly. "We've got them, Baldassara."

"You think so?"

The others are gathered around us, grey shapes breathing clouds into the cold air.

"Five minutes," says the Gaffer.

Somewhere to our right, the lieutenant is bringing the remaining sections of the platoon into position. Beyond them, the rest of our company is moving up. And on our left, out of sight, is B Company. The battalion is under strength. We've lost a lot of men since Sicily, to the Germans and sickness. But we have more than enough to take a village, I guess.

Colle d'Anchise, as it shows itself in the grey dawn, is tiny. A single street stretches out before us with a row of houses on either side. We move forward carefully through someone's vegetable patch, conscious of the noise we make each time we step on a twig or kick a stone. We stop again at a point where the dirt path we're following meets the road.

"Are they all sleeping?" says Derrick.

"Are there even any Germans?" says Paddy.

"Keep your voices down," says Strong John.

We wait. A runner hands the Gaffer a piece of paper, waits for an answer and then departs. I gulp water from my canteen. Paddy checks his rifle's magazine. Derrick mutters a prayer.

At 0610 hours, we stand in line and on a signal from the Gaffer move forward at the double. I hear the sound of boots pounding stone, the creak and rustle of leather and cloth, and the men's soft breathing. And then, as we spread out, the noise we make grows softer. My face is coated in sweat. Danny is jogging beside me, his rifle in both hands. Sunlight flashes off the bayonet that's attached to it. I have my rifle at the ready too. We stop at the third or fourth house we come to as the others move past us. I glance up and down the street, first to one side and then the other. Inside of a minute our men are in position, poised to knock down doors and start shooting. But for an instant we stand still, as if we can't believe that it can start like this, in the quiet of an October morning.

And then there's a whistle, the *crack* of a rifle, a shouted command.

Mayhem erupts.

I blast the lock. Danny grabs the handle, swings the door open and I charge inside.

"Gottverdammt!"

"Schweinepriester!"

A half-naked German appears in a doorway. He's red-faced and white-haired, struggling to pull up his pants with one hand, raising a pistol with the other. Danny steps up, swings the butt of his rifle at the German's head, then slashes and lunges, killing him instantly. Another shouting figure comes into view, this one at the top of the stairs; there's another one behind him. I shoot once, twice, three times in their direction. The first one is down. I shoot again. The second one trips, bumps and rolls screaming down the stairs, his hands flailing wildly, clutching at the posts, grasping for something to hold on to. Danny swings his rifle round menacingly and the German, groggy-eyed, lifts his shaking hands above his head. I search him quickly for weapons and motion for him to go outside.

We check out the house without saying a word. Danny darts through the downstairs rooms while I stand back, covering him. He does the same for me upstairs as I kick open doors, turn over beds and poke my nose into cupboards. There are no more Germans. No civilians either. Just the two of us and two corpses.

Downstairs again, I almost lose my footing on the smooth wooden floor. Danny catches and holds my shoulder.

"Steady!" he says.

Hand-to-hand fighting is shocking. It happens so fast. You hear yourself yelling. Your muscles get tight. And the other guys — the ones who are trying to kill you — you see their rage and the fear in their faces. You see their eyes open wide when they're struck and then go dull as death darkens them.

And afterwards you feel empty. You don't even notice the adrenaline that pumps through your body when the action begins, but when it's over, you're drained. It's all you can do to stay standing.

* * *

We clear the houses on one side of the street. B Company works the other side. Not all the Germans are as sleepy as the ones Danny and I encountered. The snap of rifle fire and the rattle of machine guns can be heard nearby. Most of it comes from behind the curtain of houses on the high side of the mountain. The enemy is still out there.

We're jogging down the street, following the others to the yard behind the captain's command post, when Danny lets out a yelp.

"Aw, crap!"

He has one hand on his neck. His face is screwed up in a grimace. There's blood leaking from between his fingers.

"Let me see," I say.

Whatever struck him — it might have been shrapnel or stone from a ricocheting bullet — has left a ragged 3-inch-long cut under his ear. I give him my handkerchief. He presses it against the wound and we start jogging again towards the far end of the street. Danny swears softly to himself the whole way.

"You're lucky," says the medical corpsman at the command post. "It missed the artery."

"I feel lucky," says Danny. He was getting over the shock of being hit. "I'm pretty sure this is my lucky day."

"I'll have it stitched up in a jiffy," says the corpsman. "Are you feeling dizzy? The cut's pretty deep. I can send you back to the RAP."

"Nah," says Danny. "That's okay."

Later, I wish he *had* accepted the corpsman's offer to go to the regimental aid post. But it's like Danny to stay. He was never a quitter, Danny. No one ever called him that.

* * *

D Company, on the other side of the mountain, gets held up for a while. And the Ontario Tanks, which were supposed to help us hold the summit, get bogged down by the river. We can't always count on the tanks to show up. But we can count on the Germans.

The first wave of enemy infantry comes at us at around 1600 hours. As we half expect, they're backed up by Panzers. By 1700 hours Danny and I and the others are holed up in a house in the middle of the village. A German tank has a bead on the house next door and for sure it will find us soon. Strong John Stonechild has the Bren gun upstairs, with Derrick feeding the ammunition, while the rest of us are shooting from the windows below. The Gaffer, Paddy and Doug face the street while Danny and I have our eyes on the hill behind us. I don't see how we can stay here much longer.

Sure enough the Gaffer turns, sees me and signals that he wants Danny and me to slip out the back. We'll take up positions to cover the others when they retreat. I tap Danny's shoulder. He wheels around and there's something about the way he looks at me. He's pale and for a second he seems not to understand me. This isn't like Danny. He's always so quick on the uptake. The bandage on his neck is soaked in blood. Seeing where I'm looking, he touches it and shrugs.

"It's fine," he says. But his voice is thick.

I go first and Danny follows me. I make it to a low stone structure, a chicken coop. I pause and look back. I don't know what makes me turn around at that moment. There's so much noise — the crash of the enemy's cannons, the smack of rifle fire and the crackle of machine guns — it's not as if I hear the shot that strikes him. But I turn.

"Danny!"

He's sprawled face-down in the dirt. Not dead: I can see him moving. I run back. Paddy and the Gaffer join me and together we drag Danny to the chicken coop. There's no chickens — the Germans made sure of that. Strong John appears behind us and gives us covering fire. We haul Danny inside and strip off his tunic. It's bad. You can just about put your fist through the hole in his back. The Gaffer goes to work silently while the other guys call out encouraging words.

"Hang on, Danny!"

"We'll get you out of here."

The Gaffer applies pressure to stop the bleeding. He administers morphine for the pain. Danny's face is contorted and his body twisted. He makes an awful gurgling noise as his lungs fill up with fluid. His eyes are wide open but he's looking past us at something we can't see. His hand is cold in mine.

"You'll be okay," I say. "You're going to make it."

It seems like an hour goes by before the Gaffer says what I know already.

"He's gone."

There's a bang, a cloud of smoke and dust, and the sound of something heavy hitting the ground behind us. The Panzer is blasting the house we were in. We have to move in a hurry.

Chapter 2

Going to War

October 1942 – October 1943

I knew Danny for just over a year. I was closer to him than I was to anybody. Losing him was like losing a brother. The army is like that: it brings people together and then it takes them away in an instant.

Three years ago, back in Red Deer, the Mounties took my pa to an internment camp in Kananaskis. They didn't take everyone who was born in Italy, just people they thought were Fascists. They never told us why Pa was arrested. He couldn't have cared less about the Fascists! We heard about Benito Mussolini when he took power in Italy. My parents got letters from relatives in the old country. But no one paid much attention to politics. It was the same when Adolf Hitler became chancellor in Germany. We had other things on our minds, like bringing in the harvest on my uncle's farm and keeping the shelves stocked in the store. Pa was too old to be a soldier, and I was too young when war was declared between the Allies and the

Axis powers — Germany, Italy and Japan. It all seemed far away.

They may have picked on Pa because he was a reader. We had a lot of books at home. The Mounties took the books when they took Pa. They let him go after a few months when they decided he wasn't dangerous. It was awful when he was gone. He sent us letters, but the guards at the prison camp read what he wrote and blacked out whole sentences. Meanwhile, we had to look after the store without him.

The store was Pa's life. He worked for the railroad for years to save up the money to start it. He was busy before it opened every day, checking stock, placing orders. He stayed late every night, going over accounts and making sure the place was tidy. We all helped, Ma, me and my sisters, Gia and Anita. I always hated working in the store, but we kept it going while he was gone. It was such a hard time. We were puzzled at first, and then we were angry. But we were scared too. People started looking at us funny, like we might be traitors. Some kids at school stopped talking to me.

We knew about the war, of course. We followed the Allies' progress in class. We knew about the Blitz over London, the U-boat war in the Atlantic and the struggle for Africa. Pa came home in the summer of '41. That winter, the Eighth Army relieved the siege of Tobruk. The United States entered the war after the Japanese attack on Pearl Harbor, and the German general, Erwin Rommel, started his second offensive in the African desert. In the spring, the news was still pretty bad. In the summer, General Montgomery took command of the Eighth Army and the war in the desert began to turn in favour of the Allies.

I enlisted in the fall of '42. I told Ma and Pa I wanted to prove that I was a good Canadian — that we all were. But that was only part of the reason. I wanted to get out of Red Deer. I wanted to get away from the hateful looks of suspicious neighbours. But there was more to it than that. I wanted a bigger life. I thought it would be exciting to go to war. I wanted to find out if I was brave. I know better now. I know more about war, but I still don't regret my decision.

So I hitched a ride into Red Deer and found my way to the armoury, headquarters of the 20th Field Regiment. I took my .22-calibre rifle with me, the one I used to hunt rabbits and squirrels. I had an idea that if I showed them that I could handle a rifle, they'd enlist me right away. That's how green I was. A grinning corporal pointed the way to the orderly room, where I found the warrant officer poking at the keys on a typewriter. I started to pull the rifle from its leather case. He glanced up. He didn't even ask me how old I was. He just growled, "We don't take kids!" and went back to typing.

But when I was on the way out, the grinning corporal took pity on me. "You really want to do this?" he asked.

"Yes," I said. "I really do."

"You might have better luck with the Eddies," he said, "if you don't mind marching. They're looking for recruits. You'll have to go there though. To Edmonton."

I had to get him to explain what he meant about marching. I didn't know how armies were organized, the difference between artillery, which is what the 20th Field Regiment was, and an infantry regiment, like the Edmontons. It was more complicated than I had imagined.

"And by the way," he added, as I set out for the train station. "Lose the rifle."

"Really?"

"Baby stuff," he said.

It turned out the Eddies were, in fact, recruiting. No one batted an eyelash when I said I was nineteen, though it was two years north of the truth. I had smudged the date on my birth certificate, but they hardly glanced at it. Soon enough — so soon it surprised me — they shipped me off to England.

Pa could have stopped me from going. He wanted to, I know, but how would it look? They might think he was undermining the war effort and send him back into detention. So he let me go.

* * *

When I was in school, I hung out with guys who liked what I liked, who shared the same interests as I did. The army's different. You get close to the men in your unit whether you want to or not. Of course, being close isn't the same as being friends. It's like family that way. You're stuck with the people you're related to. But Danny and I were friends.

I arrived in the south of England in time to take part in a series of exercises. We landed on beaches, climbed cliffs and took part in war games. It was all new to me. I had been plunked down in the unit to fill a hole left by soldiers who had been transferred out or fallen sick. Most of the rest of the battalion, the men I was training with, had been in England for a year or more. They'd been through scores of lectures, drills and route marches, and had a much better idea than I did about how to survive on a battlefield. Without them, I wouldn't have lasted an hour.

They all played a part in my education. The Gaffer is regular army, a Brit who moved to Canada, and a lifer, not a volunteer. A lot of lifers look down on those of us from civvy street who signed up "for the duration," that is, until the war ends. Not the Gaffer. "Doesn't matter to me," he says. "If you can tell your boot from your butt and walk upright, that's good enough. I can do the rest."

I got to know the others in my section gradually. Strong John Stonechild kept to himself, but whenever I was in trouble, like struggling to manhandle heavy boxes, he was there to give me a hand. The O'Connor brothers are a pair of cheerful Irish toughs. Paddy worked in a warehouse before the war and Derrick was a cook. Baby-faced Doug McDonald is ever-so-quietly efficient, a good guy to have in your corner. And then there was Danny.

He was a farm boy from Alberta. His parents emigrated from Poland, and mine from Italy, but it seemed like we had lots in common. He liked reading even more than I did. But he was handy too. He could fix anything — if the army had any sense at all, he'd have been a sapper. He'd have been good at building bridges and planting mines. After the war he wanted to be a racing car mechanic and take part in endurance races, like the LeMans 24-hour. It's a big deal in France. I'd never heard of it but, because Danny was crazy for it, I wanted to see it too.

These were the guys I got to know best. We saw a lot of the captain, of course. Captain Trehan has a round face, pink cheeks and thick eyebrows. He keeps an eye on us. He's smart, I think, and doesn't put on any airs. The Gaffer looks up to him, which means a lot. Lieutenant Gold is a fan of the captain too. Gold was a bookkeeper before the war and he's a stickler for detail. I often see him poring over papers and maps. I like the way he thinks about things. One time, when we were still in England, I was doing guard duty. He caught me reading a book. He gave me heck, but then he asked me what the book was. Turned out he had read it too.

"I can't quarrel with your taste in literature," he told me. "Just, you know . . . "

"Sir?"

"Don't let me catch you slacking off again."

* * *

They called it "hardening." What they meant was that the training we went through in England was like nursery school compared to what they put us through next. In May 1943 we boarded the train for Scotland. For the next six weeks we were made to work as we had never worked before.

In England, we were sent out on cross-country marches. In Scotland they made us run. In England, we practised unopposed beach landings. In Scotland they fired live ammunition over our heads. In England, we honed our bayonet skills by lunging at straw dummies. In Scotland, a commando unit from the Royal Marines showed us how to kill with our hands.

The Gaffer loved it. "Maybe, just maybe," he said, "you lot will be of some use, after all."

We got one last week off in London. And then we went to war.

* * *

We sailed for Sicily at the beginning of July. We made it through the campaign there together, Danny and me. We survived the heat, the mountains, the dust and the disease. At one time nearly half the company was down with malaria or jaundice. And then there were the Germans.

After Sicily, the landing in Italy in September was easy. And the push from there was a steady slog against an enemy that mostly used hit-and-run tactics. It wasn't fun, but it wasn't as vicious as Sicily had been, at least until we got to Colle d'Anchise, where we fought off the Panzers until the Ontario Tanks arrived too late to save Danny.

Chapter 3
Baranello
October–November 1943

Sometimes the army just ticks you off.

Colle d'Anchise was two days ago and we're supposed to be moving on. There are five or six outfits all snarled at a single crossroads. A bunch of MPs and NCOs are waving their arms and insisting that their unit has the right of way. Hundreds of vehicles are jammed together. Engines are roaring, gears are grinding and nothing is moving. Typical army.

And the weather stinks.

We've found an old barn not far from the road that still had some roof on it. This gives us shelter from the rain. The Gaffer brews tea. In the afternoon, Paddy and Derrick set off to see what they can scrounge for supper. There are no hot meals coming our way in this messed-up situation. We'll be cooking for ourselves or eating compo rations. Eventually the boys come back with bread, a few eggs and hard cheese. "All I need to make an omelette," says Derrick cheerfully. In the meantime, I write letters.

I write home. That's easy. I tell them I'm fine and that I'm not seeing much fighting. I complain about the food and the weather. It's what they want to hear and it's what I want to tell them. Then I write a letter to Danny's parents, which is really hard. Danny had showed me pictures of them: his mom, with her apple cheeks and soft eyes, his dad, with his bushy moustache and high forehead. It's going to be tough for them to carry on, knowing that Danny is gone. It's going to be tough for me.

Finally I write to a girl Danny got to know at the Beaver Club in London. I know she really liked him. She told me. There's no way she'll know he was killed if I don't tell her. I wish I could tell her myself, in person, but who knows when I'll be back in London?

Maybe never.

* * *

We've got reinforcements!

The traffic jam was sorted out, finally, and we got shifted into this mountaintop village, Baranello, for a bit of rest and recreation. I've been given a billet in a barn with chickens. It smells bad, but headquarters says I'll be sleeping with the poultry for only a few days. Meanwhile, three men have been added to our section, all of them as green as grass.

The old man among them is Jimmy Philpott. He's tall and gangly and never stops moving. He never stops talking either. It's hard to tell if he is scared or just too eager to be friends. He says in civilian life he was the foreman on a road gang.

Doug thinks he's been in trouble with the law. "He just looks like he's had a hard life," he says.

"Well, he looks strong enough, at least," says Paddy. "I'm not so sure about the other two."

The youngest of the new arrivals is a fair-haired, moon-faced kid named Leonard.

"He lied to get in, for sure," says Doug as soon as he sees him. "No way he's turned eighteen."

He does seem young. Also soft and simple-minded. He says the only job he ever had was grocer's messenger, which figures. I can imagine him delivering groceries, but the idea that he might be able to kill someone . . . Even the Gaffer looks doubtful. Derrick has given him a nickname. He calls him Loon.

The third recruit, Ray Toppi, is a pudgy man in his twenties. He wears wire-rimmed glasses that make him look like an inquisitive mouse. Because of the glasses, of course we'll call him Specs. He was a lecturer at the university in Edmonton. He seems surprised to be here.

"Well," says Doug to the Gaffer, "you made

soldiers out of the rest of us. I guess you can work with this gang."

The Gaffer makes a face. "Job's not getting any easier," he says.

* * *

I've been moved out of the barn. My new home is an outbuilding with a loft, which I share with Doug. The quartermaster's crew has rigged up a couple of cots in the loft, making it snug. We share the building with two mules and a horse, but they don't bother us. The old man who owns the place, Benedetto, would be happier if we didn't know about them. He's worried the army will take them away.

Brigadier General Vokes has taken over the division from Simmonds, which makes him a Major General now, I guess. Vokes is like the Gaffer, a regular army guy, but the Gaffer is not a fan. He says Vokes is a conceited blowhard.

"Monty is Monty," says the Gaffer, meaning General Montgomery. "He wears his beret in a certain way and carries that fly swatter as a swagger stick. But when Vokes walks around with a fly swatter too, well . . . "

"He just looks like an idiot," says Derrick, finishing the Gaffer's sentence.

"He's a good officer," says Gold.

Both Gold and the Gaffer like the new brigade commander, Brigadier Hoffmeister, who has taken over from Vokes.

Lieutenant Colonel Jefferson stays in command of the Eddies, but they decided to change our name. It seems that calling us the Edmonton Regiment wasn't good enough; now we're the *Loyal* Edmontons. We've been buddies with the British Loyal Regiment (North Lancashire) for years, and we spent a winter in their barracks when we were in England. So I guess the change is meant to underline the linkage.

"Doesn't mean we weren't loyal before," says Lieutenant Gold.

"Glad he cleared that up," mutters Derrick.

* * *

Today there was a fight. It had nothing to do with the Germans.

A bunch of us — the O'Connors, Strong John, Doug and the new boys — got a day pass into Campobasso, the nearest town, three or four miles down the road. The rear echelon, with help from the Salvation Army, has fixed the place up for our benefit. There's a movie theatre, a men's club and a handful of canteens They're calling Campobasso Maple Leaf City because the Canadians have taken it over.

We played darts at the club and then ate at a café. Afterwards, we wandered around until we found ourselves on the edge of town. A boy, about eight or nine, was standing in an alley between two houses. He gestured for us to follow him.

"What the heck?" says Paddy. "We've got nothing better to do."

He's a skinny kid. I catch up to him and give him a chocolate bar I've got in my tunic. He takes it and sticks it in his pocket.

The kid — he tells me his name is Gino — leads us on a twisty path past fields and an olive grove to a barn. Only it isn't a barn: it's been turned into a sort of club.

"Hey!" says Jimmy. "How about this?"

There are lanterns on the rafters. The floor is beaten earth with straw laid over it. There are rough wooden tables and benches pulled up around them. In the corner, an old guy is playing the accordion. There are about twenty Canadians already here. I spot Freddy Whitelaw and a couple of others from the Seaforth Highlanders. Freddy sees me and waves me over.

An older woman is serving wine. Some of the men have been here for a while. They have that look on their faces that Pa and his friends get when they've been drinking.

"This is more like it," says Jimmy. Paddy and Derrick seem to agree. Loon looks worried and Specs looks interested. Together they take over a vacant table. Doug and I head over to where Freddy Whitelaw is sitting.

I've had wine at home. I've had beer since I joined the army.

"Go on," says Doug. "It won't hurt you."

"Okay," I say. "Why not?"

Freddy has pals at Brigade HQ. He tells us the Germans are making a stand along the Trigno River. This is part of the Winter Line we've been hearing about, where the Germans mean to stop us from advancing any farther. Freddie's friends say the British 78th Division is getting beaten up pretty bad.

"Here's to the 78th," says Doug.

"May they give as good as they get," says Freddy.

We put down our mugs and are thoughtful for a moment. Then Freddy says, "Whatever happens on the Trigno, you know they're resting us up for a reason. We're next."

"That's right," says Doug.

I feel sad all of a sudden. I tell Freddy about Danny Kurlowicz. Since we stopped in Baranello, I've been thinking about him a lot. About his parents and his girlfriend. And not just about him. So many others have been hurt, taken sick or died.

"The enemy is always in front of you," I tell Freddy. "You see him coming. You see death coming, if you know what I mean — either his death or yours. It's not a surprise."

"Huh," says Freddy.

"But your buddies are beside or behind you. When they get hit, it's sudden and secret, sort of. You turn around and see them. It was like that with Danny. I turned around and he was on the ground. Too fast for me to feel anything."

The wine is affecting our mood. Or maybe, now that we aren't marching or fighting, or even waiting to march or fight, we're thinking of things we haven't thought about for a while.

There's a commotion across the room, where we left Paddy, Derrick and the others. Jimmy is in the middle of it. We hear stray words above the din.

"Bloody Eddies," says a Seaforth Highlander.

"Where's your skirt?" sneers Jimmy. He means the Highlanders' kilt.

"Shut your gob!"

"I'll shut yours . . . "

They start to push each other. Paddy's on his feet, trying to separate them. One of the Highlander's pals gets involved and soon he and Paddy are pushing too. I wonder if I should be helping Paddy, but Freddy is unconcerned.

"Idiots," he says. Both he and Doug stay seated, so I do too.

Some men like to fight. I saw it in England when the guys got bored. Others stay out of it. Jimmy's in the middle of this one. He throws a punch and takes one to the chin. It seems to surprise him. The O'Connors are brawling too. Soon there's a dozen men involved. The fighters are in the middle, the rest of us around them, thinking the fighters will soon wear themselves out. Then someone throws something. One of the lamps is knocked down from the rafters and the straw on the floor catches fire. It happens so fast, at first we don't see how bad it is. There's a flash and then flames. The fight ends in an instant. A couple of the boys try to stamp out the fire, but it spreads too fast. The barn fills with smoke and everyone scrambles for the door.

A few of us stay and watch as the barn burns down. There's no way to put out the fire. We stand with the old guy, his accordion now silent at his feet. The owners, the woman and her husband, stand beside us. She's sobbing; he looks grim. Gino is off to one side. I watch as he takes the chocolate I gave him out of his pocket. He unwraps it carefully, breaks off a chunk and starts to eat.

The next day Jimmy is called up before the

captain. According to most reports, he was the one who started the fight. He's one of those guys who gets mean when he's been drinking.

Meanwhile, for the rest of us, all passes into Maple Leaf City have been cancelled until further notice.

* * *

It snowed! I didn't know it snowed in Italy.

It came on suddenly, a blizzard of wet snowflakes carried on a swirling wind. While it lasted, you could hardly see ten feet in front of you. When it lifted, a thin white blanket coated the cobblestone streets.

Now, a few hours later, all traces of snow are gone. But gosh it's cold!

To keep them busy, Hoffy has organized lectures for officers: Lieutenant Gold disappears for hours each day. The rest of us are put to work as well. Two hours of exercise and drill in the morning and then an hour on the rifle range. It turns out Specs is a pretty good shot. Jimmy isn't bad, but Loon is struggling. The Gaffer tells me to help him out.

"You're a natural," he says. "It's a waste of bullets, you practising. See what you can do with the youngster." Funny: He's not much younger than me.

All the lectures, exercises and practices have a

purpose. The 2nd Canadian Brigade is going back to war. And, judging by what we're hearing, with the British 78th making slow progress against the enemy, we'll have our work cut out for us. The Germans are making a stand.

A couple of days later, Doug asks me, "What would you have done if the Italians had kept fighting beside the Jerries?"

"I would have fought them," I say.

Doug has a habit of blinking when he's thinking. It's like something he does to get his brain ticking over.

"I knew when I signed up that Italy was on Germany's side and that both were our enemies," I told him, "but I didn't think much about it. I guess I didn't think about them as people, you know? I didn't think of them as people my parents might know."

"Is that likely?" he asks. "That your parents know people who're fighting with the Fascists?"

"I dunno," I say. "My dad left Italy long before the Fascists came to power."

"Would it make a difference if you knew someone? Someone on the other side?"

"Why would it? They're the enemy."

"But they're people too."

"They're all people," I say. "Under the uniform,

they're all people, just like us. Doesn't really matter if we know them, does it?"

Doug blinked some more. Then he said, "It's better just to think of them as the enemy."

* * *

"Is it a donkey or a mule?"

Sometimes you ask a question thinking you're the only one who doesn't know the answer. Then you find out no one knows.

The brigade decided that instead of a regular sports day before we go back into action, we're going to have donkey races. The O'Connor brothers have been put in charge of finding our donkey and Strong John has been chosen as our jockey. If the donkey won't move fast enough, says Paddy, then Strong John can carry it instead.

But no one knows the answer to my question. This doesn't stop them from pretending they know.

"A donkey is an officer, of course. All officers are donkeys. Everyone knows that."

"They're both failed attempts at a horse."

"A mule is an enchanted donkey. Kiss it on the lips and you'll see."

"Will it turn into a donkey?"

"No, a princess. All you have to do is kiss it."

It's the lieutenant who finally comes up with an answer.

"A donkey is a species of African horse," he says. "A mule is a cross between a horse and a donkey."

I'm not sure that this is true, but it doesn't matter. Donkey or mule, it can still be entered in the derby.

Later, Gino and I go off to see Benedetto. Benedetto is proud of his donkeys. Or mules.

* * *

According to Freddy, the British 78th are making a push to the next river, the Sangro, where the Germans will make another stand. The 78th are supported by divisions from India and New Zealand. They're taking a lot of wounded and a lot of dead.

In other news, it turns out the brass hats are coming to see us. Not just Vokes and Hoffy, but also the Corps commander, General Crerar, and Ralston, the minister of national defence.

"You have to figure they're getting ready to kiss your you-know-what goodbye when they organize a parade to see you off," says Derrick.

The padre wants us to have questions ready for Ralston. He says Ralston wants to chat with us informally. You know what everyone asks first? "When do we go home?"

The padre just says, "Come on now, boys. Get serious."

When the day arrives, the minister, James Ralston, and General Vokes review us together, Hoffy and Jefferson trailing behind them. Vokes is strutting and full of himself. Ralston is impressive. He turns out to be a short, stout man. He was an officer in the last war and he knows how to handle himself on a parade ground. He looks us all square in the eye, taking his time, sometimes asking a question. And afterwards, he has us stand easy around him.

It seems like he really wants to know what we hope will happen after the war. Some of the guys give thoughtful answers. We all know what it was like before the war, when jobs were hard to come by and the prairies turned to dust. And now the fighting. I guess it's important to think about what comes next.

* * *

On the morning of the Donkey Derby I set off to see Benedetto. He looks worried. He's afraid that once the army gets its hands on his mule, he'll never get it back. I have to promise I'll make up for it if anything happens.

It's a crazy scene at the sports field. Everyone knows the holiday is just about over, that we're going back to war real soon. There's a lot of yelling and laughter as each company gathers round its mule before the races.

I try to enter Gino on Benedetto's beast. If he wins, then the prize money goes to Gino's family, so they can build a new barn. The race marshal won't let me. Another regular army jerk. He does let me take up a collection, though, and Gino is happy with that. Our entry, Becky, doesn't win. Strong John can't understand it: he was sure he and the mule had an understanding.

Turns out the Gaffer bet against him.

"What the heck, Sergeant? How could you bet against Strong John?"

"Well, lads," he says. "It's all about making smart choices." And he walks off chuckling, like he's pleased with himself.

* * *

The padre has the biggest-ever turnout for a church parade. It's a cold, wet day. All through the service, the men shift their weight from one foot to the other, trying to keep warm. Everyone joins in the hymn-singing, our voices strong, if off key: "Oh, God! Our help in ages past / Our hope for years to come . . . "

That afternoon, the Gaffer gets us together in a corner of the men's club in Baranello. Rain splashes against the windows, but there's a fire in the fireplace and the chairs are comfortable. He somehow got his hands on two cases of beer, which he leaves open on the floor. Suddenly I remember Monty's speech to the brigade back in August. "Do you have enough beer?" he asked us. The men roared out the answer: "No!" Funny thing is, he promised us more, but we never got it. It went to the Seaforths instead. That was the rumour anyway. Those guys get supplies no other unit gets.

"Drink up," says the Gaffer.

Jimmy finishes one bottle and reaches for another.

"If there's anyone who loves you lot," the Gaffer says, "you should write to them today."

"Who're you going to write to, Loon?" asks Jimmy. He makes it sound as if no one could love the kid, like it's a joke.

Loon answers quietly. "My ma," he says.

"What about you, Jimmy? Who's waiting for you to come home?"

"No one," says Jimmy flatly. "I got no ties. No worries. I'm a free man."

No one has to ask the red-headed O'Connor boys who they write to. We've all seen pictures of their family.

"What about you, Doug?" I ask.

"I'll write to my dad," he says and blinks. "My mom died last year. Now my dad is on his own. And you?"

"Ma and Pa get anxious if they don't hear from me," I tell him.

I also write a letter to Strong John's parents. He tells me what to put down. It's not that he can't write it himself, but he says his handwriting is bad. He says he hates to send home letters that look like they're written by a child.

I don't know why he asks me to do this, but I don't mind. It's not too much to ask.

* * *

Gino is waiting for me on our last day in Baranello. I haven't told him we're going, but the kid seems to know our plans. Good thing he isn't working for the Germans. The two of us walk together to the mess tent and the kid sits down with us. He doesn't cry or anything. I make sure he has a plateful of bangers and eggs. Doug tells him cheerfully that the eggs are made from powder and the sausages filled with sawdust, but the kid goes away with a full stomach, at least.

Lieutenant Colonel Jefferson was summoned to a Brigade Operations Group yesterday. Battalion O Group was held this morning. We're getting our marching orders. It won't be long now.

Chapter 4
From the Moro to the Gully
December 1943

The holiday's over.

The sky is black and the rain is coming down in sheets when we leave Baranello.

We scramble on board what the army call Transport Carrying Vehicles — TCVs — which means they can be anything from a donkey cart to a flat-bed truck, and in this case turn out to be ordinary canvas-covered two-and-a-half ton trucks. We pass through Campobasso and half a dozen other towns and villages, all the while getting bounced like popcorn in a can.

Twice we stop and scatter when Stukas, their guns blazing, swoop low over the road. The staging area is an open field. Bed is where we make it.

"Sleep tight," says Jimmy. He's new to this. Maybe the dive-bomb attack is the first time he's been shot at. He looks shaken.

The war is getting closer. We can hear and sometimes see it: a flash on the horizon, a dull rumble in the distance.

The next day we board the trucks again. There are more enemy aircraft overhead: twice we stop and scramble for cover. We pass another eight butt-aching hours on the road. The noise of war is still ahead of us.

* * *

It's December 2 and conditions are miserable. We cross the Sangro River in near-total darkness between 0100 or 0200 hours, tramping over a Bailey bridge that's been thrown together by the engineers. There's the sound of rushing water beneath our feet, a cold black sky above us. Cold rain dripping from our faces. We walk in single file, the lieutenant leading the way, followed by Doug, the O'Connors, Strong John, then Loon, Specs and Jimmy. The Gaffer brings up the rear.

We pass the wreckage of battle as we move forward, the massive shadows of banged-up tanks and trucks; bundles that might be bodies or abandoned backpacks.

"Stay on the marked path!" the Gaffer calls out. The sloped and muddy fields on either side of us have not yet been cleared of mines.

Another staging area, another hot meal under canvas. It's quieter now. The war noise is receding as we advance. New rumours find us at every stop. Jimmy collects them as if they're clues to buried treasure. As if knowing where we're going determines what happens next.

"There's another river ahead of us," he says.

Other voices chime in. "More than one. The River Moro and then the Arielli."

"Nothing but rivers."

"It's the east–west road that matters. The road to Rome."

"The Brits are pulling out tomorrow," says Jimmy. "I got it on good authority."

"The 8th Indian Division is on our flank," says someone else.

"The Brits are going to Rome?"

"Not the 78th. They've had it."

Doug, who has been silent, sits down beside me.

"What do you reckon is happening?" he asks.

"Nobody knows nothin'," I say.

* * *

The next day we shift camp a few hundred feet for no obvious reason. Maybe it's just to keep us warm. The 2nd Infantry Brigade is gathered around us, the Seaforths on one side and the Princess Pats on the other. The 78th Division is just ahead. The colonel summoned his second-in-command to a nearby town, San Vito Chietino, for a meeting in the morning. They come back looking important. They know something and we don't.

Jimmy's chatter continues without letup. "Gaffer says to keep my rifle clean. It's clean. When is it ever not clean?"

"You'll be glad when the time comes."

"Did you see the Gurkhas? The knives they carry are wicked."

"They're fierce, those guys."

"Hey, Loon. Have you heard from your girl?"

"They're building a supply dump at San Vito."

"Oh, I forgot. You don't have one."

"Shut it, Jimmy."

Another day, another move. We cross yet another river, this one called the Feltrino. Then we stop on a bit of level ground. There are olive groves and patches of forest all around us. The trees give us cover from enemy aircraft. They also give us some shelter from the weather. Seems like there are troops everywhere. Most of them are ours, but the lieutenant says the Germans are around here too. He said they're making a stand along the Moro River. That's about half a mile from where we're camped.

Later in the morning, as if to prove that the lieutenant knows what he's talking about, small-arms fire erupts from someplace to the west of us. And then the rattle of machine guns. The Gaffer doesn't have to order us to scratch out a slit trench in the stony ground. No one gets much sleep. The captain has the company secure the perimeter. The Princess Pats are on our left flank and beyond them, the 1st Brigade is settling in. The Seaforths are on our right, and the 3rd Brigade is between them and the sea. Everything is in place for us to move up later to take over from the last remaining units of the British 78th.

There are quiet spells in the night when I nod off, and then, just as my chin settles onto my chest, I'm startled awake by a burst of machine-gun and mortar fire, whistles and shouts. At one point a flare goes up and I see Doug in the trench next to mine.

He mutters something I can't quite hear, then clears his throat and tries again. "Is this what you expected when you signed up?'

"I thought it would be warmer."

"It may get hot in other ways."

This is a dumb thing to say, but we are all getting kind of nervous.

Later in the night, Vokes sends patrols over the river. Units from the Seaforths and Princess Pats poke about on the other side. The Hasty P's send a party over too. Their sector covers a road that skirts the coast. The lieutenant says there's a plan.

There's always a plan. What happens is something different.

* * *

Another day in limbo. The Seaforths are slated to attack the middle of the front, towards a village, San Leonardo, while the Princess Pats strike on the left or western side towards another, smaller village, La Torre. When these objectives are taken — in a few hours if all goes well — it'll be our turn to move through the Pats' position towards a crossroads, which has been given the name "Cider." From there we're to swing to the east and take Ortona, a port on the coast.

Nothing to it.

Later in the evening, elements from the 1st Infantry Brigade move in behind us, ready to take our place when we advance.

* * *

Monday night is not the kind of night you would normally choose for fireworks. It's raining heavily. Everything is wet. We make our way into an abandoned barn and, in spite of the rain, there are fireworks.

Both the lieutenant and the Gaffer take the time to check weapons, packs and ammunition. Jimmy, all bundled up in his groundsheet and looking pale, takes apart his rifle and cleans it without being told. And then he does it again.

Strong John is very still, the way he gets before going into action.

"Are you praying?" I ask him.

He shakes his head, no.

"Then what?"

"I was thinking about home."

It's almost time. There are tanks grinding their way into position behind us. Men, mules, mortar and machine-gun companies are being organized. Runners trudge through the darkness. And then it's quiet again as midnight approaches.

It stays quiet for some time.

And then the fireworks start.

A dozen machine guns open up on the other side of the river. Mortars bang away. The noise gets louder and more intense, and then it stops suddenly. There's a pause, another rattle of machine-gun fire and it all starts up again. It goes on all night. We hear a scream at one point and men shouting. And then the noise dies down again.

In the morning, the supply company brings us rumours with breakfast. There are a dozen wounded at the regimental aid post. The Seaforths have taken prisoners. We hear different numbers. Tanks were unable to cross the river; it was too muddy and soft. The battle is going well. It's going badly. We will be moving soon. We'll be holding our position.

We don't move. Not in the morning. Not in the afternoon. We wait in the rain and listen to the noise of battle. Eventually, in spite of the uproar, some of us fall asleep wrapped up in our groundsheets. And then finally, in the evening, we get the call.

"Come on, you slugs! Rouse yourselves!"

"Shake a leg!"

Jimmy has disappeared. Strong John finds him slumped behind a wall. Strong John reaches down and lifts him up with one giant hand. Jimmy looks dazed.

"I was sleeping," he says.

We join the rest of the company and wait in the shadows of an olive grove until a guide finds us. Orders are passed along the line and we start making our way towards the front. The ground falls away beneath our feet. The going gets slippery. There are frequent flashes in the sky that look like lightning, but that's not what they are. The crashes aren't thunder either. They're artillery. We cross the river. Any part of us that isn't already wet is soaked by the time we get to the other side. We scramble up the steep embankment and form up again in a shivering line.

And then we're told to go back.

Our job was to follow up on the progress made by the Princess Pats, to push on through the objective after they had taken it. But their objective, La Torre, is still being contested. Without progress, there's nothing to follow up. We turn around and splash across the cold black river.

Nothing goes according to plan.

* * *

It's Wednesday — more than a week since we left Campobasso — and no one knows what's happening. No one, that is, who shares the information with us. Rumour has it that the tanks were unable to cross the river because the engineers were unable to build a bridge across it. It was impossible, they said, because the banks were too steep. Without tank support, the attackers were unable to hold their position on the other side. The Princess Pats have been pulled back; the Seaforths too.

About a dozen men are dead, wounded or missing.

Meanwhile, the 8th Indian Division has taken over from the Princess Pats on our left flank. Rumour has it that they built a bridge where our engineers couldn't. Vokes — who's an engineer — must be furious.

Seems like everyone but us has been thrown into battle. The Hasty P's, the 48th Highlanders, the Seaforths and then the Royal Canadian

Regiment all have crossed over to the other side. The lieutenant says we should be ready to move tomorrow.

* * *

We cross the river for the second time on Thursday night. On the other side we're joined by a mortar platoon and a squadron of Calgary tanks.

The Seaforth Highlanders lead the way again into San Leonardo, only this time, they take the village and hold it. Again our task is to follow through towards Cider Crossroads. When we control the Ortona highway, the enemy is expected to pull back to the next big river, the Arielli. At sunrise we're in the village — not that there is much of it left. Most buildings are scorched and empty shells. The street is strewn with rubble and wreckage. Dead Germans lie where they fell. Their pockets have been turned out by souvenir-seekers, their holsters are empty and their belts have been removed. Some of the men collect German bayonets and the *Gott mit uns* — "God is with us" — belt buckles.

"Want a little something to remember San Leonardo by?" says Jimmy. He means to sound casual but his voice is strained.

Loon, with his round, white face and pale eyes, stares straight ahead.

The barrage begins at 0900 on Friday morning. Kittyhawks make their roaring sorties overhead. And then the artillery kicks in, not just our guns but some Indian arty as well. The Royal Navy is doing its part too, tossing enormous high-explosive shells in front of us from the guns on a pair of cruisers offshore. The noise is shattering. The smoke is blinding. The ground shakes: I feel the vibrations through my boots and calves and up through my stomach and chest. We haven't seen anything like this since we landed at Pachino.

The Gaffer has the platoon paired up. Strong John and Jimmy, Paddy and Derrick, Doug and me are put together. The Gaffer keeps an eye on Loon and Specs. Somewhere off to the right the other two sections are moving into position, along with the lieutenant and captain. And with the captain there's a forward observation officer from the 3rd Field Regiment and a radioman. A Company is in position and ready to go.

We push off at 0945 hours.

The barrage walks in front of us at a steady, almost brisk pace. There are plenty of small obstacles — boulders and bushes and the rocky beds of small streams. The ground is soggy where it isn't muddy. The barrage is making it worse.

It's hard to keep track of what's happening

now. It's like I've walked into a different world. The air is filled with smoke, dirt and dust, and the ground is pitted, broken and hot where shells have landed. The ringing in my ears fills my head. I hear everything, I hear nothing. I can see no more than a few yards in front of me. I'm like a robot, a mechanical being, my senses dulled. The rifle in my hands is weightless. I see my buddies fire their weapons but they're noiseless. Even the deep-throated rattle of Doug's Sten gun gets lost in the thundering row.

I see Jimmy on the ground, Strong John kneeling beside him.

The branch of a tree flies past me. It brushes my sleeve. Above me, a plane disappears into the billowing smoke. I can't tell if it was hit or was diving at the enemy's line.

I crouch behind a low stone wall. Doug is beside me.

There is a Sherman tank a hundred feet behind me. Its machine gun is spurting fire. We march on. The smell of cordite stings my nostrils. My eyes are dry and sore. The rifle is cold in my hands. There has been no reason to shoot. I have seen no German soldiers. Just the flash and drifting smoke from mortars and medium machine guns.

The Gaffer trots by and punches me on the

shoulder. Loon lopes along at his side. Specs struggles to keep up with them. I move as if in a dream.

And then the smoke lifts. The noise dies away. I hear the Gaffer shout, "On your left!"

The barrage hasn't stopped, but it has leapt ahead of us. The ground closest to us becomes visible as the smog lifts. The guys from the platoon are strung out around us. Strong John is on the ground, firing the Bren in short bursts. Jimmy lies flat on the ground beside him. I can't see what Strong John's shooting at, but I instinctively bend low as I move up beside him. I slip into a muddy ditch and peer ahead.

Mortar and machine-gun fire is coming from a line of scraggly trees on our left flank. The barrage is coming back from the enemy's side. The ground explodes all around us. Stone chips and shrapnel ricochet into the brush. I think of Gene Krupa, the drummer in Benny Goodman's big band, banging away at his cymbals and drums. The staccato of the snare drum and the thump of the bass are echoed in the weapons being used against us. The noisy confusion is complete.

I glance at Jimmy. He's curled up on the ground in the fetal position. His face is wet, his eyes squeezed shut.

Figures are moving in front of the line of

scraggly trees: German soldiers. Bees buzz past my head. The bees are bullets. The Gaffer's shouting at us. "Move! Don't sit there! *Go!*"

I move, keeping close to the ground. Doug and Strong John are behind me. Strong John has the Bren gun in one hand. He's dragging Jimmy along with the other. The Shermans are moving up behind us, pumping shells at the enemy. I run, stumble, take cover and get my bearings, and then run again.

The Germans are rushing towards us, just as we are rushing at them. They have their Mark IV Panzers behind them. Their barrage stops as we come together and the close-up fighting begins. The ground is rough. I never see more than a fraction of the battlefield. I never see more than a handful of the enemy at any one time, but the racket of small-arms fire is everywhere. A Grenadier pops up suddenly from a fold in the ground. A German tank appears from behind a stone hut, another from behind a stand of trees. We stalk one another. It all happens so fast, too fast for my brain to process, too fast to keep track of.

At last, I take cover behind a tree and snipe at the enemy. I see the Gaffer yelling in Loon's ear, Loon nodding his head in agreement. Specs is crouched behind a stone wall, reloading his weapon.

There's an almighty explosion behind us. One of the Shermans takes a hit. Its magazine blows up. Parts fly in all directions. In an instant, all that's left is a blazing, blackened chassis. The crew has no chance.

* * *

When you're in a firefight, it can seem as if everything is out of control: one random event follows another without rhyme or reason. But the captain is behind us, monitoring the situation. The forward observation officer is calling in arty and air support. The lieutenant keeps in touch with the captain and so keeps his platoon in touch with the company. And the Gaffer is tireless, the ends of his moustache twitching as he lurches from point to point, checking on us.

Another Sherman takes the place of the one that was destroyed. We keep moving forward, quickly at first, and then more slowly. In the course of the day we advance, at most, a few hundred yards. Eventually we repel the German counterattack. We lose three tanks. Enemy patrols and occasional sniping make us cautious. We never get close to Cider Crossroads.

Late in the afternoon, Strong John is leading us up a narrow dirt path through rocky country. He's bending forward instinctively to avoid presenting too obvious a target. Machine-gun fire breaks out as soon as his head rises above the height of the land. We halt. Captain Trehan comes up for a look-see. With the lieutenant beside him, he peers through binoculars at the prospect on the other side of the ridge. What lies in front of us is a deep ravine, less than half a mile wide, that runs all the way to the sea. Exploratory parties are sent off in different directions. All come under fire from concealed positions. We dig in.

All of us, that is, except Jimmy. He's sent back to the RAP. The tag attached to his tunic says *Battle Exhaustion.*

The next morning, all three A Company platoons, ours included, are out patrolling the edges of the Gully. Elements from the whole brigade are involved: the Seaforths on our left flank, the Princess Pats on our right. Division HQ figures there's a weakness somewhere in the German defences. The lieutenant says the enemy has 88-mm anti-tank guns dug into the opposite bank, along with tanks and self-propelled arty. Pretty much the whole darn shooting match is sitting there waiting for us.

And no one knew they were there.

* * *

Doug plops himself down beside me in the evening.

"You got a girl waiting for you back home?" he asks.

"There was a girl," I say.

"Is she waiting for you?"

"I don't know. Maybe."

Bella is the daughter of one of Pa's best friends. We've always been close to her family. I've known Bella forever, but it's not like we were going steady. Not exactly. I like her a lot, and she likes me. I don't know if she'll wait and I don't know if I want her to, but she gave me her picture before I left.

I pull out my wallet and show Doug.

"Wow! She's something!"

"Yeah, I guess so," I say. We're digging into compo rations and washing them down with tea the O'Connor brothers have made. Doug takes a swallow and sputters.

"What the heck, Derrick," says Doug. "You ever think of using this on the Jerries?"

"Drink up," he answers. "It'll put fire in your bones."

Derrick and Paddy sit down with us and then Strong John joins us too.

"Hey, Strong John! What happened to Jimmy?"

"Was it something I said?" asks Doug.

"He's scared," says Strong John.

"He was scared from the get-go," says Derrick.

"Some guys just get worn down," says Paddy. "The stuff you see and the stuff you do."

"Sure," says Derrick, "but . . . "

"With other guys, it's all in their heads. It's not what happens, it's what they're *afraid* will happen."

"The anticipation," says Doug.

"But anticipation isn't the same as battle exhaustion," says Derrick.

"So, what you're saying is, he's yellow," says Doug.

"Do you think so?" I ask.

"I dunno," says Doug. "We don't know much about him. We don't know what he's been through."

"I think he's seen some things," says Strong John. "He's had a hard life."

Strong John has had a hard life. He would know.

"How about you, Paul?" says Derrick, turning towards me. How come you're so cool?"

"Yeah," says Doug. "I saw you shooting that rifle of yours. You might have been shooting rabbits. What goes through your head when you're shooting Jerries?"

I say, "I let my mind go blank. Isn't that what you do? You see something move. You shoot." What I don't say is that I never feel cool in a firefight. I feel numb.

"Yeah," says Doug. "But for me, there's a

moment before I pull the trigger when I'm scared. I mean, I'm shooting someone."

"Well," says Derrick, "you'd better get over that."

* * *

It has started to rain again. We emerge from our trenches into a dark and drizzly dawn. All day, rain drips off the rim of my helmet. My tunic's soaked. It's impossible to keep my socks dry. The sound of small-arms fire breaks through the damp air at intervals. It's hard to tell where it's coming from or how far away it is.

We keep sending out patrols. The Germans send out their recce parties too, some of them slipping in behind us. It's our turn one late afternoon. We follow a path that's little more than a dirt track. We hear the crack of a rifle, branches shiver and stone chips zing past us. No one gets hurt. We never see who's shooting.

After another nearly sleepless night, we wake up to see the sun for the first time in what seems like an age.

It's Monday, December 13. At around 0630 hours, two companies of the Carleton & York Regiment pass through to where the Germans are dug in. We wish them luck. Half an hour later, the barrage begins. The enemy is stuck into the near slope of the Gully and our arty shoots over them. Even where there are German guns on the other side, they're so deeply embedded that our shells don't touch them. Even the mortars aren't doing the job.

In the afternoon the Carleton & York return. They were badly mauled.

* * *

Back from another patrol, I run into Freddy Whitelaw looking beat-up but happy. He says his unit took Cider Crossroads.

"Oh, yeah," I say. "So how come you're here and not there?"

"Let me tell you," he says.

"Uh-huh."

"We set out this morning with a squadron of four Shermans. We aimed to find a way around the top of the Gully instead of going straight at it, like the Carletons. We found a track and followed it. The weather was foul. The mud stuck to our boots and the boys in the tanks were worried that they'd get stuck, but they kept up.

"The captain called a halt when we were close to the Gully. He said there weren't enough of us to win a set-piece battle, but that we might pull it off if we took the Jerries by surprise. And he laid out his plan.

"We fixed bayonets. We spread out in a line. Our tanks were drawn up in line behind us. On his signal, we charged."

"You did *what*?" I say.

"We charged. We started screaming and charged down the side of the Gully." He shakes his head at the memory.

"Well, the Jerries *were* surprised. They popped out of their slit trenches like prairie dogs out of their holes. Hands straight into the air! It was all we could do to round them up.

"Some of them made a fight of it, mind you, and destroyed one of our Shermans. It was all over in minutes. We took more than seventy prisoners."

"Seriously? Seventy?"

"Maybe even more. We sent a party back with the prisoners. And then we set off for Ortona."

"You made it to the crossroads?"

"It got a bit tense. We started up the far side of the Gully. We'd lost the element of surprise and were meeting resistance. We lost radio contact with the battalion. And we lost two more Shermans. But, yes, we made it almost all the way to the crossroads. The lads were all fired up and wanted to keep going. Of course, we couldn't, not really.

"Our last tank got stuck. The squadron commander said he had no choice but to destroy it — those were his orders. Without the radio, there was no chance to call up more support.

We had to pull back. But it was an adventure, Paul. It was a good day."

* * *

Two companies of the Carleton & York are sent into the Gully in another attempt to fight their way through to the other side. The Germans send them back again. Vokes keeps trying. He's a stubborn cuss.

Lieutenant Gold comes back from brigade HQ with news that the 22e Regiment — the Van Doos — have taken the same route as the Seaforths did yesterday in an attempt to go around the top of the Gully. The Germans sent in reinforcements overnight and are making a fight of it. The Van Doos are under a lot of pressure but, at last report, were holding their position near Cider Crossroads. We may get there yet.

* * *

The barrage continues. Again, the Carleton & York is sent into the enemy's mouth. And again, it gets chomped on, chewed up and spat out.

I watch as the stretcher bearers bring back the wounded and dead. The retreat is orderly, but horrible to see. Even Lieutenant Gold mutters something about mad orders and out-of-touch commanders. The Gaffer, who is not known for being diplomatic, calls it a monumental cock-up. "Vokes," he says, "should be shot."

* * *

Jimmy just turned up.

We're in a farmhouse on a bit of high ground. From behind the stone wall that surrounds the yard, there's a view over a patch of the Gully. This is our observation post.

"I've got something for you," Jimmy says, and he drops a mailbag on the kitchen table.

"Also this." And he produces a kitbag packed with goodies, including cigarettes, chocolate and socks sent by women's auxiliaries back in Canada. "You can thank the rear echelon," says Jimmy. "They said since I was headed this way, I might as well bring them."

"I could use some socks," says Derrick.

"How're you doing?" I ask Jimmy.

"Why are you asking?" he says. Right away he's defensive.

"Where did they take you?" asks Doug.

"How's life behind the lines?" asks Paddy.

"Planning to stay this time?" adds Derrick.

Jimmy turns red and it looks as if he's going to take a swing at someone. The moment passes and then Jimmy seems to get smaller. It's like the juice has been wrung out of him. "Regimental aid post," he says. "San Vito Chietino."

"Hanging out with the nurses, eh?"

"Have a good time? We've seen some fighting."

"They treat you okay?" I ask.

"The MO gave me something to make me sleep."

"That's it?"

"I slept for two days."

"On a nice soft bed, no doubt," says Derrick, still mocking him. "With nurses to fluff up your pillow?"

"That's enough," says the Gaffer. He has been watching and listening.

"I needed a break," says Jimmy. There's a pleading note in his voice.

Strong John has been listening too. Now he gestures to Jimmy "We're going to need you," he says.

"I'm here to stay," says Jimmy defiantly. And that's that, I guess.

* * *

On Wednesday, December 15, word reaches us that most of the Van Doos C Company has been wiped out defending a house, Casa Berardi, on the road to Ortona. Somehow the survivors held on until a squadron of tanks arrived. There's something brewing in our sector now. Lots of activity at Brigade HQ.

* * *

Maybe we'll remember today, December 18, as the day we break through the Gully. I sure hope so. Another barrage opens up at 0700 hours. Elements of the 1st Canadian Infantry Brigade are moving up on our left behind the arty in yet another attempt to take Cider Crossroads. They're following the route the Seaforths and Van Doos explored earlier. Finally Vokes has stopped sending our guys straight into the mouth of the Gully. We're going around it instead.

That's what we hear. We wait, but it's not our turn yet.

We've got a blazing fire going in another abandoned farmhouse. We're gathered around it like hunters. Only, instead of wolves howling in the darkness, our background noise is the staccato of small-arms fire and the thunder of guns. We've eaten supper, if you can call compo rations supper. We've brewed tea. A couple of the guys write letters until dusk takes away the last of the daylight. Now there's only the glow from the fire. Most of the men are sitting on such furniture as there is, or propped up against the wall. I can't settle down though. I start poking through cupboards.

"People live here," I say. "You forget sometimes."

"Maybe it's best to forget about that," says Paddy. "It's not our job to look out for civilians."

"But they're around," I say. "We buy stuff from them."

Derek laughs briefly. "When we remember to pay," he says.

"We take over their homes. Where do you suppose this family is?"

"They're better off anywhere but here," says Paddy.

"My sister has a doll just like this," I say, holding it up. "My ma brought it with her when she came to Canada."

"What's up with you, Paul?" says Derrick. "It's a *doll*."

"I dunno," I say. "Sometimes the war just seems so messed up."

"You think we need to be reminded?" says Derrick.

I can't stop thinking about it. Civilians are everywhere around us. Some are glad to see us. They bring out bottles of wine and call us liberators. They tell us where there are Panzers and German machine-gun nests. Others are surly. They're the ones who supported the Fascists, I guess. Some must have been in the army. Instead of surrendering, they stripped off their uniforms and threw away their rifles. Now they're wondering what happens next. Others get in our way and get hurt. It isn't only Germans who are killed by our bombs and guns.

Doug understands what I mean. Specs seems to get it, though he doesn't say much. He's still trying to figure out how the heck he got here. But paying attention to the people in the streets doesn't mean we're soft. At least, I don't think it does.

* * *

On Sunday, 1st Brigade consolidates its position at Cider Crossroads and the road that leads to Ortona. And suddenly everyone is on the move. Word has it that the Seaforths are taking over the coast road from the Hasty P's, while the 3rd Brigade is being pulled back to recover from their losses. That leaves us, 2nd Brigade, to chase the Germans back to the Arielli River.

Not that the going gets easier. Apparently the Grenadiers are being pulled out of the line by the German high command. They're being replaced by the 1st Parachute Division — Hitler's favoured few, fanatical devotees of the Führer. The Grenadiers were tough enough. The Paras are even tougher. That's what the Gaffer says.

Chapter 5
The Road to Ortona
Monday, December 20, 1943

On Sunday evening, Lieutenant Gold tells us the Germans are pulling out of Ortona. This is the word coming from Division HQ. The Germans haven't fought to hold onto any other city in Italy, so why would they fight to hold this one? That's what headquarters thought. Turns out they're wrong and the Germans are staying put. We will be fighting them in the streets.

Captain Trehan stopped by and spoke to the lieutenant. The lieutenant passes on the news. "The 1st and 3rd brigades have seen heavier fighting than we have up to now," he says. "That's about to change."

No one is surprised. Just about every other unit had taken more casualties than we have in recent days. The army likes us to suffer equally. It's our turn.

"There's only one way into Ortona," he tells us. "The town is bounded by the sea on the north and on its eastern sides, and by a deep ravine on the west. That leaves only the road we've been fighting for over the past week. This road enters the town from the south.

"We're obviously not going to surprise them. What's more, they're battle-hardened and they've had a few days to prepare for us. Some of them have seen action in Africa and on the Russian Front. They'll make us pay for every inch we take."

He stops to take a breath.

"Why don't we go around them?" asks Specs. "Can't we cut the town off?"

"The 1st Brigade will be moving up on our left flank. And the Indian Division is beyond them, on the other side. They should be able to cut off the German supply line north of Ortona eventually, but in the meantime, we've got our assignment. We're going for the enemy's throat."

A figure of speech. What the lieutenant means is that we'll try for the quick kill. Stop the enemy in his tracks. That's one way of looking at it. Of course, it could also mean that the enemy's about to swallow us up.

* * *

The forming-up position is about a thousand yards past Cider Crossroads. From there to Ortona is less than 2 miles. This ground has been the scene of fighting for two weeks. The Desert Air Force has bombed and strafed it. Our arty and the

Germans' have blasted it. Even the Royal Navy's guns have had a go at it. Add the damage done by tanks, mortars and heavy machine guns and the battlefield looks like a scene from the Great War. This is No Man's Land. Trees stripped of their leaves and branches. Buildings reduced to a few burnt beams and broken stones. An occasional chimney where once there was a fireplace and a family gathered around it. Now there's nothing, no sign of life. The carcasses of mules and horses are strewn at random on ground pocked by explosives and churned up by tanks. The slippery earth reeks of garbage and rotten flesh. And this is what it looks like before we begin our advance.

At 1200 hours we start moving behind another barrage. D Company is on one side of the road, B Company on the other. C Company has linked up with the Seaforths who are coming up the coast. We start out with Battalion HQ. Two troops of Three Rivers Tanks and a company of Saskatoon Light Infantry machine gunners come with us, together with a company of sappers. We're feeling pretty good. Glad not to be stuck on the wrong side of the Gully anymore. Glad to be on the move. This isn't a recce patrol or a probe into the enemy's defences. This is an advance in strength.

For a while, it's easy, a walk in the park. The

arty puts down a billowing black curtain ahead of us. The tanks groan and crunch the earth beside us. The sappers scan the ground for mines in front. Everything is moving the way it's meant to, until one of our tanks hits a mine. The explosion blows the Sherman 20 feet into the air.

We plod on for more than an hour. Then, as we get closer to Ortona, the barrage eases up. The idea is to keep the town more or less intact. The lieutenant says Monty wants the harbour for shipping and he wants the town as a base for the winter. He doesn't want it flattened. So our big guns stop shooting as we get closer and the smoke starts to clear.

Now we can hear shouted commands.

"More mines ahead!"

"Don't bunch up!"

Our route is mainly flat. The mines the sappers have missed are barely camouflaged under little heaps of earth and grass. You can spot them as long as you pay attention. We keep our heads down as we trudge ahead. Our packs are heavy with rations and ammunition. Our tin hats are secured by chin-straps that graze our cheeks. Our weapons are at the ready. We come under sniper fire and then, as we get closer to the built-up area, German machine guns open up somewhere to the right.

I can see bits of the town: a grey stone mass piled onto the promontory. Beyond it, I catch a salty whiff of the Adriatic Sea. Between us and the town there's a narrow road criss-crossed by dirt tracks leading to farms and cottages. Suddenly we're caught in a crossfire. The *zip* and *pop* of sniper fire and the rattle of a machine gun push us onto the ground.

The Gaffer calls out, "Check the man on your right!"

I glance at Doug.

"Anyone hit?" yells the Gaffer.

Half a dozen voices, one after the other, answer, "No!"

A minute later the Gaffer crawls up beside us. Loon and Specs are just behind him. "Where's it coming from?"

"There's a house," I say. "At about 2 o'clock. On the right."

"How far?"

"Thirty or forty yards."

"What do you reckon they've got?"

"At a guess, an M-34 Mauser."

"And the other?"

"Can't tell where he is," says Doug. "He's got us in his sights, though."

"Loon!" says the Gaffer. "What now? What's our move?"

Loon looks stunned for a moment. He's used to asking questions, not answering them. He stutters and then stops and thinks.

"A flanking movement, Sergeant?"

"On what? The sniper?"

"The machine gun."

We're hugging the dirt, all five of us. There's not much cover. I lift my head slowly, glance around and then duck again as a bullet kicks the mucky earth in front of me. There's a flat field in front of us. On the far side, a low stone wall and beyond it, an orchard.

"The sniper's behind the wall," I say. "The trees at the back of him make it hard to pick him out."

"Smoke won't cover us," says the Gaffer. "The breeze is too strong. We'll have to work our way around."

He glances our way. Doug and I nod.

The Gaffer and the new boys start crawling towards the machine-gun nest. Doug and I head the other way, towards the sniper.

It takes time to reach the edge of the field. The Germans keep banging away. Sometimes it seems like they're firing at random, but then a volley comes too close and you know they've seen something: a blade of grass move, or the crown of a helmet.

I keep elbowing my way forward. There's a half-buried pie plate inches in front of me. "What the . . . ?" And then the penny drops: it's a Teller landmine and I damn near banged my chin on it.

We make it finally to a dip in the field and a broken-down cart in the corner. Doug pulls himself up into a kneeling position behind the cart. I wriggle under it.

"What have you got?" I ask Doug.

"I can see the Gaffer," he says. "Or his pack and helmet. He's close to the German position."

"And the sniper?"

As if in answer, I see the flash from the muzzle of a rifle just above the low stone wall.

"Did you see — ?"

"Got it," I say before Doug finishes the sentence.

We hold our fire, but not for long. There's a sudden movement on our right. It's Loon, rising up, lurching forward. At that instant, I glimpse the sniper as he pokes his head above the fence. I let loose one round and then another in his direction. Doug fires a series of bursts at the enemy emplacement. Loon is weaving his way on a zigzag path towards the farmhouse. Someone has to tell him you can't dodge bullets. Doug keeps on firing in bursts from his Sten gun. I shift to a kneeling position and squeeze off another round. Loon is closing in on his objective.

"Now, Loon!" mutters Doug. "Throw it *now*!"

The Germans are shooting back. Some of their fire is coming our way.

Loon's very close. From where I'm crouched, I can see him silhouetted against the building.

"Now, Loon, now!"

I'm on my feet. The damned German behind the wall is still shooting. Now everything happens at once.

I fire another round at the sniper.

Doug runs towards the house.

Loon's grenade explodes inside it.

"Got him," I mutter. The sniper is motionless on the ground. Doug, loping towards the others, reaches into his webbing for a spare magazine and reloads. The German machine gun is silent.

Somewhere on our left I hear one of the others shout, "Let's go!"

"You okay?" says Doug. "It doesn't usually take you three shots."

"How many bullets did *you* use?" I ask.

He blinks and smiles.

* * *

We're on the edge of the town. On either side of the main road there are small fields, big and small houses separated by stone walls, olive groves, grape vines and narrow dirt tracks. Civilians pop into view from time to time. An old woman dressed in black looks out fearfully from the window of a tiny house. A shoeless boy in a ragged shirt flits from a garden to a doorway and back. A baby cries.

Loon has a different look about him. There's a swagger in his step and, at the same time, a sober set to his mouth. He threw a fragmentation grenade and then saw the result, the mutilated bodies of the German defenders. The Gaffer, striding beside him, seems satisfied with a job well done.

I reckon, however, that the day is far from over.

The company on our left is getting blasted by artillery that seems to be coming from the middle of Ortona. The noise from that side is getting louder as we draw closer. The Seaforths, on our right, are taking fire from a church tower. We've been forced by enemy fire to stay off the road. We climb fences and clear houses one by one. In a couple of hours we advance, at the most, a couple of hundred yards. Our line is getting ragged. We can hear other sections on either side of us, but it's hard to locate them. There's a danger we'll get cut off or lost.

In late afternoon we stop and regroup. Captain Trehan comes by for a visit. Later the Gaffer tells us what's up.

"Things are not going according to plan.

There's an enemy strongpoint over there," he says, indicating our right flank. "The Church of San Costantinopoli. The Seaforths are dealing with it. It may take them a while.

"Over there," he continues, now pointing to our left, "things are getting hot. Machine guns, sniper fire. The enemy is bringing medium machine guns to bear.

"We need to pull our line together, to consolidate. We've got the Saskatoons behind us, along with the tanks. The colonel has established his CP in a villa and is calling an O Group for later. He wants to get our firepower, the tanks and machine guns, properly involved in the fight.

"So this evening," says the Gaffer, "we dig in."

We brew tea and sample our rations. Then the Gaffer sends us out on patrol. "Keep your heads down," he says. "Watch out for booby traps. We'll report back here in an hour."

In this part of town, there are walls around every little property. Every cottage has its garden, small orchard or grape vines. With visibility so limited, it's easy to see why the Gaffer's worried about us losing touch. Doug and I make our way into the yard behind a house with Strong John and Jimmy. The Gaffer, Loon, Specs and the O'Connors are checking out the place next door.

We wave at them and keep going.

We barge through doors and peer through windows. It's strange to tramp through a town like this. Mostly we've fought in the open. Now in abandoned kitchens we find dishes on the table, food on the counter — all signs of interrupted lives. Outside, there's smoke and dust swirling on the horizon, the sound of small-arms fire and shells exploding. In another garden, we peer cautiously over the wall before climbing it.

"After you." says Doug softly.

"No, no," I reply. "After you, I insist."

Doug hauls himself over the top and I follow.

"Can you see Strong John?" he asks.

"Over there." I nod in the direction of another wall, another house.

We're guided by the noise, the staccato of small arms from the church on our right, the rumble of artillery ahead and to the left. We haven't seen the Gaffer for some time.

"Where's Strong John?" says Doug. Strong John and Jimmy were a house away from us moments earlier.

We call out their names, neither whispering or shouting, not knowing who's within earshot. There's no reply.

There's a sudden crash, straight ahead, and the

sound of glass and stone exploding. And then another in the yard next door. We dive for cover.

Mortars!

"It's coming from the church," I yell. "Where the Seaforths are."

The church of Santa Maria di Costantinopoli looms over us. Somehow we have edged over to the right.

"Hey, Strong John!" I yell again. "Jimmy!" No one answers.

Another mortar bomb blows up behind us.

"Move it!" shouts Doug.

We scramble to the left, scale a wall, crouch in its shelter and look around. I expect to find the Gaffer's group, but the garden is empty.

"Specs! Derrick! Paddy!"

Another explosion. This one's close. A fiery wind washes over my face. And then another. The enemy is mortaring the area on a grid. We climb yet another wall.

Another explosion. This one is followed by screams.

We're looking at a house — or half a house. Where the front was, there's now an enormous hole. Figures emerge from a storm of dust. A child wails. A woman writhes in pain on the floor. Another woman stands over them. Her face and hands are bloody. Her dress is torn. She screams when she sees us.

Without thinking, I run forward, put down my rifle and kneel by the wounded woman's side.

"We need bandages," I say to Doug. "And morphine." I unhitch my pack and toss it in his direction. "See what you can find."

The woman is bleeding. Already there is a crimson pool spreading around her on the floor. An artery has been severed. I push my hand down on the wound, trying to gauge its size. I reckon I can stanch the bleeding, but soon she's going to need more help than I can provide.

Doug fumbles through my pack and tosses the first-aid kit my way.

The other woman has stopped screaming, thank God, and has gathered up the child.

"Is she wounded too?" I ask Doug.

"No."

"We could use a blanket," I say. "A coat. Something to keep her warm."

I stick the hypodermic in the wounded woman's arm and push down the plunger. Doug disappears into the house. He comes back with blankets and a bottle.

"Wine?"

"Some kind of liquor."

"Good," I say. "I can use that."

I splash it on the wound, place a pressure pack on it and then wrap bandages around the woman to hold the pack in place. She's quieter now as the morphine takes effect. I grasp one of the blankets.

"Help me with this," I say. Before Doug moves, however, the other woman kneels down and together we bundle up the casualty.

"Come si chiama?" I ask her. "Mi chiamo Paolo." *My name is Paolo.*

She stares blankly at me for a moment and then answers, "Teresa. Mi chiamo Teresa."

"Teresa," I say. "Good." Her sister's name, I learn, is Claudia. The child, Tomas, is Claudia's son. He's almost five. Teresa takes Tomas into her arms.

The sound of exploding bombs punctuates our conversation. Some are near at hand, others farther away, but they aren't stopping.

"With luck," I say to Doug, "she'll be stable until we can get help."

I turn to Teresa. "Dove possiamo trovare un medico?" *Where can we find a doctor?*

She answers immediately. She can lead us to him.

"We're taking this woman to a doctor," I tell Doug.

"You're not serious."

"What do you think?"

I hoist my rifle and backpack and then lift Claudia. I nod to Teresa and she wraps the boy in the other blanket. And then we start walking, not to rejoin the section somewhere behind us, but straight ahead. Teresa leads the way. I fall in behind her with Claudia, now barely conscious, cradled in my arms. Doug, his weapon at the ready, brings up the rear. He makes his reluctance obvious. We're disobeying orders. And worse, we're headed straight for the Germans. He says nothing; he just scowls.

* * *

It's getting dark as Teresa takes us down narrow paths and across cobblestone streets. We duck into doorways to survey the way ahead, and then plunge onwards again. Claudia moans and mutters words that make no sense. The child, either exhausted or terrified, is silent.

It seems a long journey, though we don't go far as the crow flies. At any moment I expect to hear the crack of a rifle, or to see Paras charging our way. We hear German voices on two occasions and freeze each time. Teresa and I, bent and burdened, might just be mistaken for civilians in the fading light. The same can't be said of Doug and his Sten gun. More than once I hear him muttering.

"This is nuts." And then, "What the hell was that?"

A *bang* like the closing of a car door. Or something, I don't know what. We keep going.

Whether because of Teresa's guidance or through sheer luck, we make it to our destination. She finds and opens a wooden door. Stone steps take us down to the basement. I see a lit lamp and a mass of people. I hear a gasp, a moment of silence and then a dozen voices speak at once.

A few come forward, their faces shocked and questioning. In the dim light behind them, there are others, old and worn. There are children too, babies and toddlers with wide-open eyes. I set down Claudia on a table and an old, white-haired man bends over her. Teresa releases the boy. Then she places a hand on my shoulder and explains to the others what happened. She says Canadian soldiers are entering the town.

I glance at Doug. He's exhausted. My own hands are shaking. I have blood on my tunic. I find a space and slump to the floor, my back against the wall. A woman offers me a stool to sit on, but I can't be bothered. She offers me something to eat. I close my eyes. For some time, I listen to the hum of nattering children, adult chatter and the scratch and clatter of dishes and furniture shifting in the crowded space. It's strangely soothing. It sounds almost like normal life, the life I left behind when I left Canada. And then I'm dead to the world.

Chapter 6
Piazza della Vittoria
Tuesday, December 21, 1943

Teresa shakes me. "È il momento di andare." *It's time to go.*

"What?"

She shakes me again, still speaking in Italian. *You told me yourself, you can't stay.*

She's holding a lantern. It's partly shuttered so as not to wake the people who are still asleep. In the half light, the basement is a heaving, snuffling, snoring mass. Doug picks his way towards us, rubbing his eyes, fumbling with his helmet. We hold a mumbled conference, made slow by the need to translate, either for Doug's benefit or Teresa's.

She says she will get Claudia to a hospital in the town. It's being held by the Germans but it's run by nuns and there's a doctor. Doug can't understand why she doesn't leave town — it's a war zone — but there's nowhere to go and no way to escape. The Allies are bombing the roads and railways, Teresa says, and Italian men, if they show themselves, are imprisoned by the Germans.

She has wrapped a coat around her, to cover her torn and bloody dress. She is small and brave, her pale skin emphasized by her black hair. Somehow she has recovered from the shock of the previous day's events. The set of her mouth is grim. She says she will show us the way back to where we met, the site of the explosion. And more than that, she will show us the layout of the town, where the Germans are, what lies ahead.

Ortona is on lumpy ground, mostly higher in the middle and falling off steeply around the edges. A low building on high ground gives me a view of the bits that lie below it.

There's a glimmer of light in the east when Teresa leads us through garden gates and back passages to an abandoned house. It overlooks the road that leads to the church of San Costantinopoli, which the Seaforths occupied yesterday. We climb the stairs to the second floor and she points to the window while, at the same time, touching a finger to her lips. I nod and peer out the window and see nothing but mist. I lean further forward, look down and jerk back.

"Jeezus!"

Military vehicles are parked in line on one side of the street, leaving just enough room for others to squeeze past them. Two sentries guard the entrance to a small café. There's a light inside, but thin curtains mask the interior. The fabric stirs and shadows are moving behind it. There's no doubt the café is a German command post.

On the eastern side of the house I can see another church, smaller than San Costantinopoli. Beyond it, Teresa says there's a square, Piazza della Vittoria. And leading to the square is the main road, the one that leads back to Cider Crossroads. These are the roads that lead in and out of Ortona. One goes straight to the mountains and one branches off to the coast. Now we know where we're coming from and where we're going. And what to expect when we arrive.

* * *

We're saying goodbye when they blow up the cathedral.

Teresa stops in her tracks. She turns and looks back at the town. The expression on her face is both helpless and furious.

A dense black cloud spirals from the far edge of the stone-grey town into the leaden sky. She murmurs something. I translate for Doug's benefit: "Cathedrale San Tommaso — the cathedral of Saint Thomas. They've blown up a tower next to it and brought down the cathedral itself."

Teresa is holding my hand. She speaks so rapidly I have to ask her to repeat herself.

"The Germans were afraid the tower would be occupied by their enemies," I tell Doug. "They've been threatening to blow it up for days. The priests tried to stop them."

"It's a big deal?" he asks.

"You're not a Catholic, you wouldn't understand. But yes, it's a big deal. It's an old church. It holds relics of the saint. For the people of Ortona, it's as if the heart of the town has been ripped out."

Teresa lets go of my hand and places it on her heart. She looks at us with an expression that is indescribably sad.

* * *

"You fools!" says the Gaffer when we find our way back to the company command post. Doug straightaway tells the sergeant about the events that took us out of the line. The Gaffer isn't impressed and he lets us know it: What we did is a breach of discipline. It was ill-advised. It placed us in needless danger. It puts the security of the entire unit at risk. He will discuss it with the lieutenant. They will consider whether or not to have us charged. Whether we are charged or not, he personally is disgusted. We had better smarten up. We had better do it now.

This is the short version. Doug looks shaken.

"Of course the Gaffer's pissed off," I tell him later. "He was worried. He'll get over it."

And he does. The lieutenant gives us a funny look the next time he sees us. But we hear no more about our excursion behind enemy lines.

* * *

Lieutenant Gold, back from company O Group, speaks to the Gaffer, who tells us there's a new plan. He says we did a good job taking out the machine-gun nest yesterday, but that's not the way he wants the job done. He says we need to use our firepower, to call in tanks and heavy machine guns of our own. The Gaffer shrugs when he tells us this, like the captain has a nice theory, but the Gaffer has his doubts.

The afternoon is overcast and cold. Doug and I fall in with our unit, form up and tramp back into town. Everything has been drained of colour. Winter has turned the landscape either grey or brown. We scramble through some of the same grounds, gardens and houses between the highway and the street that we went through yesterday. The Seaforths are still fighting a tough battle on our right flank. B and D companies, with tank support, are blasting their way down the main road on our left. The clatter, rumble and periodic explosions from either side never stop for long. The noise, however, moves with us as the afternoon wears on. The Germans are retreating house by house in the direction of the first square.

We make some noise ourselves as we mop up the in-between areas. But the captain was determined to proceed in a more orderly fashion than we did yesterday, so sections are keeping in touch with one another as we advance. The lieutenant is keeping track as each house is secured.

The Germans are just as disciplined as we are. You'd think they've been given the same orders as us, only backwards. There's another position behind every position they abandon. Snipers lurk on rooftops. They are quick to pick off any of our men who show themselves. Docherty's section has suffered a couple of casualties. We've been luckier, so far.

Derrick and Paddy are crouched in the shelter of a stone wall when I duck down beside them. Derrick is cursing under his breath.

"What's up?" I ask Paddy.

"Show him," he says to Derrick.

"Dammit," says Derrick.

"What?"

"Look at this." He turns around, bends over and offers his backside up for inspection. There's a 6-inch tear in the seat of his pants.

"How bloody close was that?" he asks.

"You telling me a *bullet* did that?"

"Darn right," says Derrick.

Paddy is still laughing when I move on.

The lieutenant calls up a couple of the Saskatoon regiment's machine gunners to assist in taking out a German strongpoint. He takes his time, putting our men in position to cover the attack. The manoeuvre goes smoothly, with one part of the section moving up on one flank and laying down covering fire before the Saskatoons set up on the other side. The action's over in a matter of minutes. One German is taken prisoner. Another is dead.

We move on.

I watch Strong John and Jimmy the next time we're held up by the enemy. Lieutenant Gold tells them to put their heads together and work out the best way to go on. Jimmy's the older of the two, but Strong John's got rank on him and, anyway, he's obviously the leader. Jimmy depends on him. Now that I watch them, I realize that Jimmy is calmer than I've seen him since he first arrived.

Doug and I are leaning against a stone wall. The noise of artillery and small-arms fire is constant — it's got so we only notice it when it stops. A thin mist hangs over us. The air smells of burnt cordite, damp leaves and mould.

"You like this," says Doug.

I'm not sure what he's getting at.

"I'm scared a lot of the time," he says. "But you're not."

"I'm scared too," I tell him. And it's true. When I'm not made numb by the noise of artillery, when the adrenaline isn't flowing through me, when I'm not flat-out exhausted, I'm scared. I'm so scared that if I let myself think about it, I wouldn't be able to move. So I try to think of the next thing I have to do. And the next thing. And from time to time I look up at the clouds and thank God I'm alive.

"You don't show it," he says.

What to tell him? "Every minute we're out here, I keep reminding myself, I'm still here," I say. "Every minute is a gift."

We push on down narrow alleys. We climb over walls and clear more houses. We rarely see the enemy for more than an instant. We see his handiwork though — the wreckage, the flames, the craters — at every turn.

We're within a block of Piazza della Vittoria, close to the little church I glimpsed earlier this morning when we're pinned down by enemy fire again. There's a medium machine gun situated either in the church tower or in a house across from it, and it has us in its sights. It rakes the walls in bursts. Stone chips whizz through the air.

Again, the lieutenant tries to organize the attack. "What are the chances of getting one of those Three Rivers tanks up here?" he asks.

"Street's too narrow," says the Gaffer.

The lieutenant thinks about this and then nods. "Yeah," he says. "The turns are too tight."

The square is on a height of land ahead of us. The little church occupies a corner between us and the square. The cross street below it gives us some cover, but our approach, when we round the corner, is wide open. Strong John and Jimmy start to work their way around to the left of the church. They're looking for a way in from the rear. The rest of us — the O'Connors, Specs, Doug and I — wait for instructions. While we wait, I realize we're short a man.

"Where's Loon?"

At first I don't see him.

"What the . . . ?" says the Gaffer.

Then I glimpse Loon's back as he disappears around the corner on our right. He's down on all fours. I can't imagine what he thinks he's doing.

We haven't even got a fix on the German machine gun. Our whole battalion is converging on the square. Soon we'll have other elements we can use to neutralize the enemy, but this will take time. Loon apparently has decided not to wait.

I can't let him go off like that alone.

Doug yells, "Hold it!" When I don't stop, I hear him mutter, "Damn," and I know he's coming too.

The yard in front of the church doesn't offer much in the way of cover. A couple of wooden benches, a lamppost and a damaged palm tree are all that stand between us and the church. There's still more than enough light to see Loon, who's kneeling behind what's left of the tree. I glance up and see, now, where the machine-gun fire is coming from. A hole has been blown in the side of the church. The gun is lodged in the second-storey gallery. The Germans have only to look straight down to see us . . .

I catch up to Loon. I touch his shoulder.

"What are you *thinking*?" I ask him.

He holds up a hand grenade.

"That hole up there isn't big enough," I say. "It's too small a target."

"I can do it."

From somewhere on our left, Strong John's Bren gun starts stuttering. He must have found a vantage point that gives him an angle on the machine gun. The Germans fire back at him. Loon breaks away from me. He doesn't so much run as lurch from side to side. He hurls the grenade when he's about 15 feet from the base of the building. It arcs up and for a second I'm certain he's thrown it too high. I stand up an instant before it explodes, lift my rifle and squeeze the trigger. Doug opens up with the Sten gun. We bang away at the enemy as smoke and dust drift over us.

Nothing up there moves.

I lower my rifle. I glance back at Doug. He looks shaken. As for Loon, he's grinning from ear to ear.

"How about that?" he says.

* * *

Derek is sitting bare-legged in a corner of the church we now occupy. He's mending the rip in his pants.

"You're lucky," I say.

"Some luck," he says. "That was too close."

"It's 'cause you have such a big butt," says his brother.

"Aw, c'mon," says Jimmy. "You almost had the perfect wound. Not too serious, just serious enough. We could have shipped you to a hospital in Africa. They'd have patched you up and then sent you off on a nice long leave."

"By the time you were healed, this bloody winter would be over," says Paddy.

"Heck, the war might be over. In this beaten-up country, at least," says Jimmy.

"You don't understand," says Derrick.

"What don't we understand?" I ask.

"They keep getting closer. First I got wounded in the leg. Next, at Colle d'Anchise, shrapnel dinged my helmet. Now this."

"Now what?" I say.

"That bullet grazed my *flesh*."

"Oh, Lord! Derrick — not your *flesh*!" Paddy gasps, as if horrified.

"Laugh all you want," says Derrick. "But I've got a premonition that I'm going to die."

"Aw, bull," says Jimmy.

But Derrick won't give up. "I was looking round the church earlier. I went down to the crypt, where the bodies are."

"Why?" asks Loon.

"It's like I was drawn there," says Derrick. "Death was calling me."

Paddy just shakes his head.

Later, I take a look at the crypt. Loon follows me down the narrow steps. The ceiling is so low that we both have to keep our heads down. It's so dark that we strike matches to light our way.

"What do you think, Loon?" I ask.

The space is small. Perhaps as many as a dozen raised stone coffins are arranged around it. It's strange but quiet, almost peaceful.

Loon looks around for a moment, then says, "It's creepy."

I laugh. "You're worried about what's creepy? How many people have you killed in the past two days?"

"That's different."

"Maybe," I tell him, then, "You should think more about the risks you take."

"Aw," he says. "I knew I could do it. They were shooting over us, they weren't looking down."

"The Jerries, you mean?"

"I knew what I was doing."

"It was lucky for you that Strong John started shooting when he did. He distracted them."

Loon says nothing.

"They only had to drop a hand grenade and the three of us would be dead."

Loon sighs. "That's what the Gaffer said."

He turns and climbs back up the stairs. He stumbles in the darkness. I'm not sure if he's more anxious to get away from the crypt or from me.

Chapter 7
Via Cespa
Wednesday, December 22, 1943

We know more about the town's layout now. There are two big squares — piazzas — Vittoria and Municipale, connected by the main street, Corso Vittorio Emanuele. The cathedral the Germans blew up, leaving only a shattered half-tower, is situated beyond Municipale, on Piazza San Tomasso, and beyond that, overlooking the sea, there's a ruined castle. There are other, smaller squares off to the side of the Corso, and smaller streets in between them, where the houses are huddled together and it would be easy to get lost.

Corso Vittorio Emanuele is our main axis of attack. The Seaforths are to clear the buildings on the right, or seaward flank, while the Eddies, led by D Company, will push hard down Corso Emanuele. Our company, A Company, is slated to clear the streets on the left.

This is our plan, not the enemy's plan. I guess theirs is different.

Major Stone's D Company, backed up by Three

Rivers Tanks, starts the day with a bang — a lot of bangs — by charging down the Corso. It's like a real, old-fashioned cavalry charge, only with tanks instead of horses. The men set off at the double. The Shermans are beside them with their sirens sounding and guns blazing. We've got a ringside seat in Piazza della Vittoria to see the action start. The Germans have to be shocked, with Stone's company charging at them like that, first thing in the morning. And it seems like it's working too. Within minutes our guys are a good 50 yards up the main street. They're running. They're shooting. It seems like nothing can stop them.

And then they stop.

I look at Doug. Doug looks at me. The Gaffer takes off his helmet, scratches his head, and says nothing.

"Why'd they stop?" asks Loon.

We find out soon enough as men who are closer to the action send back word. Seems the boys in the tanks lost their nerve at a critical moment. One minute the lead tank is rolling along spouting noise, fury and destruction. The next minute it's a mute and motionless pile of metal.

Major Stone's furious. He runs up to the tank and pounds on its sides. The troop commander's head pops up from the top hatch. Stone yells,

"What the *hell*?" The troop commander says there's got to be mines up ahead, which is true enough. You can see his point. But Stone doesn't see it that way. His boys figure he's going to strangle the tank commander with his bare hands, he's so mad. But the tank doesn't budge and then the Germans wake up and start shooting. It turns out they have a lot of firepower trained along the Corso. So much for the surprise. D Company has no choice but to stop and take cover.

Meanwhile, another troop of tanks sets off along another wide street, Via Pantaleone Rapino. As they come to each cross street, the ones running parallel to the Corso, they let loose a few volleys. They're shooting blind. They can't see the enemy, but they figure the Germans are down there somewhere. The fireworks are for our benefit. We're going in behind the tanks.

We set off in a loose formation. We follow, huffing a bit, our breath making clouds in the crisp air, as far as Via Cespa. We're about to turn down it when we run into trouble.

Loon and Specs are up front with the Gaffer. Strong John, Jimmy and Doug are right behind them. The O'Connors are next. Derrick is still muttering about premonitions. Paddy's egging him on, telling him what an inviting target his butt is.

"Whatever you do," he tells Derrick, "don't turn your back on the Jerries. You know they're just waiting for a chance." He's about to say something more, but before he can speak, a gun barks out from the other end of Via Cespa. We're in a line, bent over but exposed, strung out across the intersection. A chunk of the house on the corner explodes above us. The gun barks again. It's raining stones. We dive for cover. There's a muffled yell.

It's Loon. He's on the ground. There's a boulder on his back.

Specs, surprisingly, is the first to reach his side. He scuttles over, keeping low. Bees are buzzing overhead. Specs shakes Loon's shoulder. Loon's moving and cursing, so he isn't dead. Specs pushes the bigger stones off of him.

"Keep down!" yells the Gaffer.

"Bloody hell!" Everyone is shouting and swearing at once. Finally Specs grabs Loon's arm and drags him to the corner.

"What the . . . ?" Loon tries to shake Specs off.

"Get your head *down*!" shouts the Gaffer.

A minute later, we're all huddled alongside a building on Via Rapino. Loon isn't hurt, not badly. He's bruised, cut and disoriented. The Gaffer offers to send him back to the aid post in the square.

Loon dusts himself off angrily. "I'll be okay," he says.

We hunker down together. Across Via Rapino, the lieutenant and Tank Docherty's section are doing the same. Doug and I end up parked against a wall of rubble.

He says, "We've got our work cut out for us."

In the next few minutes, Lieutenant Gold and the Gaffer put their heads together. They peer cautiously around the corner and take a good hard look down the street. It's no more than 12 feet wide, 15 at its widest. The houses, made of brick, stone or stucco, are crowded together, shoulder to shoulder. Most have a common wall with their next-door neighbour, leaving no gaps for shelter. There is nowhere to hide. The houses are no more than two or three storeys high. Many have iron balconies and all have wooden shutters on their windows. At least, that's what the buildings look like that are standing.

German demolition teams have been busy. They've blown up houses at intervals all down the street. That means there are great big heaps of stone and broken beams lying around, which the enemy has used to build barricades. It's a safe bet there are guns hidden behind some or all of them. It also means that any tank that turns down the street — which would be crazy, anyway, because there's no room for a tank to manoeuvre — has to climb over the piles of rubble. If a tank does try to climb the piles, there will be a moment when its cannon is pointed uselessly at the sky and its underside is exposed to the enemy. It won't stand a chance.

"We need a plan," says the lieutenant.

For once the Gaffer doesn't crack a smile.

"It's like a game of tic-tac-toe," says the lieutenant. "They take a house, we take a house."

"I never liked the game," says Specs. "The guy who makes the first move always wins. And the Jerries got here first."

"Maybe it's not like tic-tac-toe," says the lieutenant.

He has been in touch with Captain Trehan. They agree that neither tanks nor artillery are of any use to us until we secure at least part of the street. So much for coordinated manoeuvres. This is a pure infantry battle.

"Remember your training," says the lieutenant.

"We were never trained in street fighting," says Paddy.

This is true.

"Well," says the lieutenant. "Draw on what you know."

After the conference, we're still huddled in the shelter of a house on Via Rapino while the enemy bangs away in our direction. The dust is settling on our tunics. Gravel sometimes bounces off our helmets. The Gaffer reckons they have either an 88-mm anti-tank gun or a PAK-40 anti-aircraft gun half-buried at the other end of Via Cespa.

A Bren carrier comes up with supplies, including hand grenades. Someone is thinking about us. We load up with both 36s, anti-personnel, and 77s, smoke grenades.

"We'll work with Docherty's section," says the Gaffer. "Lieutenant Gold will be with him. They'll take one side, we'll take the other."

"It's not really much of a plan, is it?" says Doug quietly.

"Plans are overrated," I say.

* * *

Someone has to take the first step into Via Cespa. We can lay down smoke, but smoke just tells the Germans when to start spraying the street with machine-gun fire. The street isn't wide and they're shooting from both sides. Every inch of the street is covered. No one wants to take that first step.

No one except Loon. The kid won't quit. He was just knocked down by debris from a damaged building and yet he's raring to go. The Gaffer shakes his head. Paddy steps up, saying he'll go first, but Loon is adamant.

"I'll do it," he says.

Docherty's section is on the left side of Cespa. We're on the right. We're to take one house, then wait for the other section to take another on the other side. It is sort of like tic-tac-toe.

Loon tosses out the first smoke grenade. The Gaffer has a hand on his shoulder, holding him back until the smoke fills the intersection. Paddy reaches for another grenade. Loon disappears into the smoke. He's been told to run to the first doorway and bust his way inside. We can hear the *thud* the butt of his rifle makes against the door. He pounds it once, twice, three times.

Doug says, "He can't get in. It's locked. It's solid."

Paddy rolls out the second grenade. The enemy keeps up a steady stream of fire. We're not shooting back. There's nothing but smoke for us to shoot at.

The thudding stops. I hold my breath. Paddy rolls out a third grenade. As it bursts I catch sight of Loon as he climbs onto a second-floor balcony.

"How the . . . ?" mutters Doug.

"The drainpipe," I say, following Doug's gaze. "He's climbing up the *drainpipe*."

The Germans see him too, just as he scrambles from the balcony into the house. Their bullets tear chunks out of the masonry. An endless minute later, we hear a crash and Loon lets out a yell, "I'm in! The door's open!"

We pile into the house and find ourselves face to face with Loon. The Gaffer takes two steps to the left and holds up his hand. A narrow passage goes the length of the house. Three doors open off it. The first door's shut.

"There's got to be a booby trap," says the Gaffer. "There's got to be. They didn't blow off the front of the house, so there has to be something."

He starts cautiously down the passage.

"Don't touch that first door," he calls out. "Stay behind me."

The second door is partly open. The Gaffer reaches out for the handle and pushes it gently while peering through the gap, checking for wire. The door swings open easily. We follow him into the kitchen.

"Don't touch anything!"

There's a full wine bottle on the counter. A chair has been knocked over. It would have been easy to grab the bottle or pull up the chair, but suddenly everything looks lethal. The Gaffer steps through the door between the kitchen and the front room, the rest of us behind him. A couch, armchairs and side tables make movement difficult. Doug edges around to the front window, stands off to the side and pulls back the curtain. I take up a position across from him, my rifle at the ready.

The Gaffer is examining the first closed door, the one nearest the front entrance, feeling with his fingers around its edges.

"Aha!" he says.

Along the top, he finds what he's been looking for: a tack and a wire tied around it.

Doug flips up the latch on the window and lifts the sash. He peers cautiously into the street.

"Strong John," says the Gaffer. "Go back through the kitchen and into the hall and check the other side of this door. Look up. There should be a charge there."

We had missed it. We weren't looking at the ceiling when we came in. We walked under a grenade fixed in place above the door. If we had pushed that first door open, it would have yanked the pin from the detonator and we would have been blown to smithereens.

"They're devils," says the Gaffer after Strong John disarms the bomb.

Doug makes a sudden move, jerking back from the window. I see a shadow, a face, an arm on the other side. No time to lift the rifle to my shoulder, so I shoot from the hip. The German makes a sound like a snarl. The potato masher slides from his grasp.

I yell, "Get down!"

The explosion shatters the glass in the window. The noise is deafening. The shock wave shakes the room. I hit the floor, stunned. I'm down on my knees. Shards of broken glass fall from my back as I scramble to my feet.

"Jeezus!"

"What the . . . "

Everyone's cursing, even Specs.

There's blood spattered everywhere. It takes us a minute to work out that it's the German's and not ours. The bomb fell under him. Loon was standing back from the window, in a straight line from the explosion. He's covered in gore.

Strong John and Jimmy take the Bren upstairs. The Gaffer checks out the basement. He comes back with the bottle from the kitchen — it wasn't booby-trapped, apparently. He opens it and passes it around.

"Good work," he says to me. "You got him just in time."

"That was close," says Loon.

He says it softly. He's still dazed. I take him into

the kitchen. I find a rag, dunk it in water and wipe him down. The blood of the enemy . . . We've all been through this, or something like it. Shooting at a distance, at long range, is one thing. But we saw the German's face in the instant before he died. Loon had the best view of all. It was only for a second, but in that instant when their eyes locked, he understood what it meant to take a life.

I ask him, "Can you do this?"

He nods his head. "Yes."

* * *

The lieutenant and Tank Docherty's section lay down smoke and, with covering fire from Strong John and Jimmy upstairs, occupy the house opposite us. The street is so narrow and the houses are so close together that it's easy to track their progress. When Lieutenant Gold gives us the thumbs-up, it's our turn to move again.

The house next to us isn't there: it's been blown up by the enemy. Paddy loads up with hand grenades. He will attempt what the grim-faced Para tried to do when he appeared at our window. The Para that died.

Docherty's crew has set up their Bren, so we have supporting lines of fire criss-crossing the street. Both our Bren gunners are searching out their opposition. The Gaffer creeps cautiously to the open front door and tosses out the first smoke canister. Paddy, crouching beside him, waits until the smoke is head-high and then steps into it. Derrick, poised to follow him, tenses up. The Gaffer touches his shoulder, signalling him to go, but Derrick doesn't move. I'm next in line behind him. I step out on the Gaffer's signal. Loon's in position to come after me, then Doug and the others.

Enemy fire is playing a violent tattoo on the cobblestones. Shrapnel ricochets off the walls. Splinters of metal and wood skitter past me. It's as if a gale-force wind is driving a storm of destruction in my direction. I want to hurl myself onto the ground, to make myself as small as possible. I keep my eyes focused on the row of houses beside me. I catch a glimpse of Paddy in the smoke ahead of me as he dekes into the next undamaged doorway. For a moment I'm alone in the desolate space between buildings. On my right, where once there was a house, there's the remnants of a wall, no more than a foot or two high, bordering the sidewalk, a scorched staircase behind it that climbs into space. The second floor is gone.

I keep going. Something pings off my helmet. I bump up against the wall of the next house and leap into the doorway. A fine grit and the stink of cordite fill the house like mist in a cemetery.

The corpse of a German lies twisted on the floor. I stumble over it and almost fall into the room. It's a ruin. I hear the sound of more shooting — the crack of Paddy's rifle — upstairs. And then shouting.

"Derrick! Up here!"

It's Paddy. He thinks his brother is following behind him instead of me.

I run up the stairs. Loon is behind me now. There's another body on the landing, another dead German. Paddy's in the front room, kneeling at the window, firing into the house across the way. Loon and I check the room at the back — there's no one there — and then I return to the ground floor to cover the others.

Doug, Specs and Jimmy charge through the open doorway. Finally Derrick hurls himself onto the floor. His face is pale.

"Made it," he mutters.

Our smoke is getting thinner and bullets are slamming into the wood and plaster in the front hall. From somewhere outside, I hear shouting. I can't make out the words. I edge carefully towards the doorway. Lieutenant Gold, in the window of the place across the street, is pointing at the house next door. Jimmy crawls up beside me.

"What's happening?"

"Not sure," I answer.

"Where's Strong John?"

"Hey, Strong John!" I yell. "Sergeant! Gaffer!"

I put everything I have into it, trying to make myself heard.

"Are you there?" I yell again.

Strong John calls back in a deep, hoarse voice, "Yeah, Paul, I'm here."

"This is bad," says Jimmy. "He's trapped."

"What do you mean?"

"He was right behind me."

"He was in the street, then?"

"He must have stumbled and taken cover in the ruined house."

Now it's Jimmy's turn to yell. "Strong John! Are you hurt?"

"I'm okay," he answers.

This isn't supposed to happen. We're meant to stick together. Now, it seems, we're strung out, with Strong John alone and under fire in the ruin next door. The Gaffer is on his own in the house we started from.

"What now?" asks Jimmy.

"I'm not sure," I say. "Smoke alone isn't enough. They know where he is."

I imagine Strong John scrunched up behind the bit of broken wall that borders the street. And the Germans taking shots at him, the lead flying inches from his helmet.

I scramble back upstairs. Jimmy is beside me. Derrick has rejoined his brother and the two of them are huddled in a corner. Doug and Loon are at the windows. I gesture to Doug. He scrambles over and I explain what's happening. Jimmy joins us, looking anxious.

"I've seen the sniper," says Doug.

"Which sniper?"

"The one in the house two doors up the way. Second-floor window, the one on the right. He's got a line on Strong John, for sure."

"Let me see if I can get a shot at him," I say.

"The angle is tight," he says, "and besides . . . "

"Yeah?"

"There's another Jerry, on the roof. Whenever I show myself, even a little, he shoots right at me."

"Take Loon's place," I tell him. "I'll get the sniper in the window, you take the guy on the roof." Doug's Sten gun is less accurate than my rifle, but a spray of automatic fire will force the German to keep his head down. If he doesn't get Doug first.

"Jimmy," I say, "you and Loon go downstairs and roll out more smoke. Give Strong John covering fire when he makes a break for it."

Jimmy hesitates. I nod in a gesture that's meant to be encouraging. Loon punches him on the shoulder — it's funny to see how much more confident Loon has become — and Jimmy follows him down the stairs.

I hug the wall and peer out cautiously. The window's glass is long gone. The wood surround is frayed and broken. The stone walls have taken a beating too. But the enemy is picking his spots: his fire is not continuous. It's almost as if he hopes to lull us into thinking he's pulled back. For a minute or two, there is nothing, and then the fusillade begins again. I look cautiously up at the roofs opposite. They jostle and overlap one another. The shooter Doug says is up there could be wedged in the shelter of an overhang. Still, to get a clear shot at either me or Doug, he has to show himself for an instant.

As for the sniper Doug says is behind the second-floor window, all I can see is a curtain.

More shouting. Loon calls out to Strong John. Jimmy yells something too. Smoke billows up from the street.

"There!" yells Doug. "Look!

The curtain stirs. I pull the trigger. Doug lets loose a blast from the Sten gun. The curtain stirs again and the barrel of a rifle emerges from the shadows. I pull the trigger a second time.

There's more shouting from the street.

"Strong John, wait!"

"Jimmy, don't!"

The smoke in the street grows bigger, as if a gaseous, ghostly monster is rising up to fill it. Doug's Sten gun burps fire. I glance at the roof and see no one. I look again at the sniper's window and glimpse a face. It pulls back. I missed my chance.

There's a sudden movement in the street. It's Jimmy. He's running at the house occupied by the enemy. He goes straight at it. Then the deep staccato voice of the Bren sub-machine gun erupts from somewhere. That has to be Strong John, joining the fray to protect Jimmy.

Jimmy's in front of the enemy-occupied house. He rears back. One hand is in front of him, pointing at his target in the upstairs window. His other hand, stretched behind him, holds a grenade. He staggers briefly and then pulls himself together, as if making a final effort. The flash from the muzzle of a rifle catches my eye and I see the German shooter on the rooftop. He's lying on the tiles, aiming his rifle at Jimmy. Doug's Sten gun erupts once more.

Jimmy hurls the hand grenade through the second-floor window. It explodes instantly.

The shooter on the rooftop lets go his rifle. It skitters across the shingles.

Jimmy collapses onto the cobblestones.

Strong John appears in the street. He stands over Jimmy, firing the Bren.

And then Loon and the Gaffer are out there too, grabbing Jimmy, each taking an arm, dragging him towards us.

It all happens so fast. Doug and I run to the top of the stairs. Loon and the Gaffer somehow drag Jimmy through the door. The O'Connors are there to meet them. Strong John, still firing his gun, backs up with the others.

"Move it!" yells the Gaffer.

"Get in!" yells Loon.

Strong John glances over his shoulder, sees the way is clear and leaps in after them. They make it inside, all of them. We're together again as a unit. All of us but Jimmy.

Jimmy is silent.

I don't know how he managed to throw that hand grenade. By the time he went down, he had been hit twice, maybe three times. More bullets struck him afterwards. We lug his body into the front room, fold his hands across his bloody torso and stand around him awkwardly.

"Damn it," says Derrick.

"And you thought it would be you," says Paddy.

Strong John sets down his gun and kneels

beside the body. He lays a big hand on Jimmy's eyelids and closes them gently.

"Jimmy didn't have to do that," says Derrick.

Strong John says, "He did it for me."

The Gaffer finds a tablecloth and drapes it over the body.

"Come on," I say to Loon. "We've got stuff to do." I slap him lightly on the shoulder.

He hesitates and then says, "Yeah."

Doug is the last to leave Jimmy's side. Doug's eyes are closed and his lips are moving silently.

"You praying?" I ask.

He shrugs sheepishly. "He wasn't easy to like, was he?" he says. "But he was brave at the end."

* * *

Tank Docherty's section takes the house next to them. Strong John, with Loon to carry the Bren gun's ammunition, provides covering fire from our side, while the rest of us take potshots when we're able. Then it's our section's turn to move out again.

Some houses are occupied by snipers; others conceal a machine-gun nest. Some are easy to get into; others are blocked. We never know what we're up against until we get to the door, and getting to the door is dangerous. Always there is the threat of a trip wire or a timed demolition charge set to blow us away.

It gets worse. The farther we move down Via Cespa, the closer we get to the first pile of rubble that blocks the street. Behind it there's a heavy machine gun and, somewhere behind that, the PAK-40 or 88 that welcomed us earlier. From time to time the enemy uses it to bring part of a building down on top of us, though he has to be careful not to take his own troops out instead.

It gets harder, but we get better. We become accustomed to running, ducking and bumping against the walls of the houses — by the end of the day, my hips and shoulders are bruised from being banged against brick and stone. We study the way different houses are constructed. We become experts at assessing which drainpipes we can climb and which will collapse under our weight. We're getting pretty good at knowing which doors can be broken open and which will withstand an assault. We go through scores of fragmentation grenades. We make good use of smoke.

We're about 45 feet — the width of three houses — from the first pile of rubble when I come up against the Flowerpot House and the Crazy German.

There's a large clay pot on either side of the door and more on the balcony. There are no flowers in them. It's December, after all. I make note of their existence ahead of time so I can avoid tripping over them. It's my turn to go first.

We lay down smoke. We counter enemy fire with fire of our own. I take a deep breath, crouch down and step into the street. The smoke envelops me. I take one, two, three . . . half a dozen fast steps, hugging the wall, glancing up in case the smoke fails. My foot strikes the first flowerpot. It's where I expected it to be. I step around it and discover that the door is slightly ajar. I'm about to kick it open when something stops me. Up to this point, all doors have been either closed or destroyed. With hardly a pause, I pick up the flowerpot, take two steps back and throw it. I pivot away to one side as it hits the door.

The door explodes. The shock wave knocks me down, but the force of the blast misses me. I look up and realize that our smoke is swirling away. There's a window above me. Its glass has been scattered. I grab hold of the shutter and haul myself inside.

Another front room. The door that connects it to the front hall has been destroyed by the explosion. I move cautiously towards it when I hear something — a *thud* and a floorboard's squeak. There's someone upstairs.

Doug is in line to follow me. I yell, as loudly as I can, "Doug, stop! Don't come in!"

More noises. Another *thud*. I back up and turn away. There's another explosion in the front hall.

"What the . . . "

Someone upstairs tosses down a hand grenade. In an instant I'm on the floor, on all fours, shaking my head, trying to think straight. Dammit! Why does this keep happening? I run through a mental checklist of body parts. Limbs and digits: check. Guts: all there. Brain: functioning. Or is it? From somewhere I hear what sounds like shouting, singing and laughter. I turn over and struggle to sit up. I try to comprehend what I'm hearing. This isn't the nervous laughter of a soldier who's been cornered. It isn't the mocking laughter of the victor lording it over the loser in a fight. It isn't even the bitter laughter of a soldier who's tired of war but making the best of it. This is the belly laugh of a man in the company of friends. Someone who hasn't a care in the world. From where I sit, with my rifle in my hands, I can see through the shattered doorway the blasted remains of the stairs and front hall. A soldier is plodding down the steps, and as he comes closer the shouting, singing and laughter get louder. He is belting out snatches of a song in German, using the sub-machine gun in his hands to conduct an invisible orchestra. He waves it, points it and occasionally fires a few rounds: *RAT-A-TAT-TAT.* He laughs. He's having a heck of a good time.

As he comes into view, I steady the rifle in my hands. And then I shoot him.

He's a big man, tall and sturdily built. He is turning towards me when I pull the trigger. Our eyes meet at the exact moment when he's hit. He looks like a beardless Santa Claus. He has a round red face and is wearing a cheery expression. There's a twinkle in his eyes. He's still singing as he swings his weapon in my direction. I fire again.

Doug steps inside as the German collapses at his feet.

"What was *that*?"

"He must have been into the vino."

"Either that," says Doug, "or he's been too long in the line. That was nuts."

* * *

The captain comes up in the early afternoon to see how we're doing. It turns out we're doing about as well as everyone else, which is to say, the Germans are fighting back harder than we expected and our progress is slower than we hoped. A lot slower. Hoffmeister is deploying reinforcements to speed things up. According to yesterday's version of The Plan, the Seaforths were told to hold down the corner of the town between the church,

San Costantinopoli, and the seashore. According to today's version, the Seaforths are going to swing around to the other side of the main axis. They will approach the cathedral and castle from the west while we move up from the south and the centre. The drive through the heart of Ortona is no longer just an Eddies show.

There's something else. They're going to bring one of the battalion's 6-pounders to the end of the street. Major Stone's company is using the guns to blow away barricades and remove snipers from rooftops — mainly by removing the roofs. With the barricades gone, along with the mines that are hidden in the rubble, and with the guns behind them silenced, we can start thinking about bringing up tanks to support us.

There's a lull while officers confer. Some of us rest while others watch the street. Paddy wanders over and looks down at me.

"Aw, Paul," he says. "Not sleeping on the job now, are you?"

"Never," I say. I may have closed my eyes briefly.

Paddy's face is creased and greasy but his gaze is steady as he sits down beside me.

"How's Derrick doing?" I ask him.

"Ah, Derrick," says Paddy. "Scared himself silly with all that talk about crypts and such."

There's a loud bang and then the sound of a shell casing hitting the floor. Specs is making himself useful, kneeling at the window a few feet from where we're sitting, keeping an eye on the street.

Paddy says, "He'll be all right."

"Sometimes," I say, half to myself, "a guy gets a feeling that his time is up and he turns out to be right."

"Yes," says Paddy. "Sometimes a lad gets that feeling."

"Danny didn't say anything the day he was shot. But he was awful quiet."

"Danny!" says Paddy. "Now there's a name I haven't heard for a while."

"He had that look in his eyes. You know what I'm saying?"

"I've seen that look," says Paddy. "It doesn't signify anything."

"No?"

"It's just fear getting the better of courage for a time. It happens to all of us."

"Yeah, I guess so."

"But this stuff about seeing the future? I don't believe that," says Paddy.

My eyes are closed again. I might even have drifted off, but another bang from Specs's rifle startles me. I glance at Paddy.

"We'll take care of Derrick, eh?" I say.

"You betcha," he answers.

* * *

They bring up the 6-pounder they promised us. Shell after shell pounds the rubble barricade and gradually it disappears. This removes a major obstacle and cover for a key German machine-gun position. Which is great. It also opens the way for an artillery duel, which is not so great. The PAK-40 at the bottom of the street, which was quiet when we engaged the enemy at close quarters, now takes on our solitary battery. The 6-pounder is no match for the enemy's gun. It's pulled out.

And we go back to work, attacking the houses on either side of Via Cespa.

So much happens, one thing after another.

I push open a door of a house and come face-to-face with a German soldier. He's young like me, smartly dressed and clean-shaven. We're both surprised. We look at one another. He has pale blue eyes and a soft mouth. I lift up my rifle. He nods his head as if to say, "Yes, you have to do that," and then he slips away in an instant. My heart is beating fast. It all happens so quickly that I wonder if it happened at all.

An old woman dressed all in black walks up the street. She picks her way carefully over the treacherous debris. She is carrying something in her arms. As she passes the house we're in, we see she's holding a tiny baby, its face as white as paper. "The kid's not moving," says Doug. I'm not sure how we know. It might have been the bleak look in the old woman's eyes, or the way she cradles the body, but we know for sure that the baby is dead.

Derrick climbs onto Paddy's shoulders to reach a second-storey balcony, while Strong John stands in the street like a fool, pouring fire into the houses opposite. Like a fool, too, I leap into the street to stand beside him. The Gaffer just shakes his head afterwards. He is either amazed by our recklessness or astonished that we're still alive. Or both.

When darkness falls, we take turns trying to sleep. It isn't easy. The noise doesn't stop and we soon figure out that the Germans aren't sleeping either. When the Gaffer comes back from the company command post, he gets shot at from a house we took earlier.

"The S-O-Bs are sneaking back behind us," he says.

It's a terrifying thought. We could be surrounded.

Chapter 8
Mouse-holing
Thursday, December 23, 1943

The sky is a lighter shade of grey when Doug kicks my feet to wake me. There's sleep in my eyes. I blink and glance up at him.

"Morning," he says.

"Breakfast in bed?" I say. "You shouldn't have."

"I didn't," he answers.

I haul myself up from the chair I've been sleeping in, amble to the front of the house and peer out the window. Fat raindrops are splashing off the windowsill and onto the floor. I'm shivering.

"It's cold enough for snow," I say to Doug.

"Might happen yet," he answers.

The Gaffer gestures for us to gather around him while we're still drinking tea and gnawing on rations.

"Gentlemen," he says, "for those of you who dreamt last night that the war was over, I have bad news." He doesn't need to complete the thought. As if on cue, we hear the banging of guns opening up from somewhere to the east of us, and the thunder of explosions as shells find their targets.

"I think they're ours," says Derrick. "Seventeen pounders."

"They're ours," says the Gaffer.

"We can go home then, I guess," says Derrick. "Leave them to it."

The Gaffer ignores him. "The captain's on his way over," he says. "Smarten up."

Captain Trehan looks careworn and as tired as everyone else. He takes the time to say a few words to each of us, though. He kids Loon about shaving, saying, "I think you missed a spot," and then points to some dirt on his cheek. None of the men has shaved recently, except the Gaffer. Like Loon, I don't need to.

"Your sergeant says you've done good work with that rifle," the captain tells me.

"I try to, sir," I say. I'm surprised. The Gaffer isn't much for passing on compliments.

"And by the way," he says to all of us. "About Philpott. His body was picked up last night. I hope there'll be a chance for you to pay your respects. But I want you to know the padre is taking care of him. He is being looked after."

The news makes me feel bad. I've hardly thought about Jimmy since he died. He said that he had no family, and I wonder if that's true. And if he had no one, I think how sad that is, to be dead and no one cares.

* * *

Under the captain's direction, we join with Tank Docherty and Boss Chudleigh's sections to launch a coordinated attack on the gun at the foot of the street. We use everything we've got, which doesn't seem like much when we put it together. The street's too narrow and we're too close to the enemy to bring in tanks or even mortars. The captain takes his time to place the Bren gunners in houses across from one another. They're well situated to suppress enemy fire. We lay down smoke and then charge in with hand grenades. The rain makes the smoke less effective than it should be and, for sure, the enemy knows we're coming. All the same, we run into less opposition than we expect. Most of it is rifle fire. The enemy gun itself, half hidden behind rubble, is silent.

Docherty, leading the way from the left, is the first to realize that the gun has been abandoned. He lets out a whoop that echoes off the houses.

"The bastards are gone!" he yells and he runs ahead of the rest of us. I can hear the elation in his voice. After everything we have been through in this town — the death, the destruction, the ever-present threat — it's amazing to know that the battle for Via Cespa is almost over. Within seconds, we're all screaming triumphantly.

"We've got them on the run!"
"Bloody Jerries!"
"It's over!"
It's the Gaffer who spots the trap.
"Halt!" he shouts. "Stop *now*!"
The captain and Lieutenant Gold hear him and take up the cry. "Don't jump! Don't go there!"
But Tank Docherty is too far ahead of us and too carried away to pay attention. He leaps onto the rubble pile and leaps again to get over it. He's a big guy. His helmet appears too small for his square head and the way he wears it, tipped back, makes his head appear even bigger. He practically wraps himself in webbing. He carries more hand grenades, ammo and supplies than anyone else does. More than anyone else can.
"Like Mussolini's medals," as Derrick once said.
I have a picture in my mind of Tank Docherty jumping over the rubble pile. He has a Sten gun in his right hand. His arms are raised high, as if he's about to take flight. There's a kind of discordant music that goes with the picture, a chorus of shouts. Some are happy, some alarmed. Not everyone hears or understands the Gaffer's urgent order.
"Don't jump!"
"Get back!"
Too late.

The entire emplacement explodes when he lands. There is no way of knowing whether the charge is triggered by a pressure plate he lands on, or detonated by a Para watching from a darkened window. Whatever sets it off, the explosion is huge. It's meant not only to kill its attackers, but also to destroy the gun completely, so there is no chance that the German weapon will be turned against them. And no chance that Docherty can survive.

We're stunned into silence. The blast burns a hole in the rain and fills the air with its hot waste. Bits of metal, stone and sand combine with dust, smoke and vapour to make a cloud that sweeps over us, and then the rain returns, and the silence ends.

"Damn it!"

"Blasted Jerries!"

We swear and scream and rage against the enemy. All at once we're shooting at everything. I see Doug rake the roofs of the surrounding buildings with his Sten gun. Others break down doors and throw grenades through windows. Magazines are emptied, the supply of grenades is exhausted. Voices grow hoarse from screaming. The platoon is out of control.

But not for long. The frenzy lasts a few minutes. Lieutenant Gold and the Gaffer round us up with a nudge and a push while the captain watches over us. He looks thoughtful and tired.

"Get over here," says the Gaffer. "Take cover, save your ammo. And for God's sake, get a grip."

We find two more Germans in the houses behind the demolished gun, one dead and one wounded. The wounded one smirks at us when Loon marches him from the house. Strong John steps in front of him and knocks him down with a punch to the head. The lieutenant steps up and grabs Strong John's shoulder.

"*Enough,*" he says. "We'll get our chance."

* * *

Captain Trehan sends word from the battalion command post in Piazza della Vittoria that he wants to see the lieutenant. The Gaffer orders me to go back with him.

"The Jerries are still sneaking snipers in behind us," he says. "We've been taking more casualties."

"I understand," I say.

"Go with the lieutenant," says the Gaffer. "I want you both back."

Lieutenant Gold and I move cautiously back up Via Cespa. We take the time to peer into every house and behind every pile of rubble we pass. We pause to scan rooftops and upstairs windows. The rain beats down on our helmets and soaks our tunics. The cobblestones are slippery under our feet. At one point I'm sure I see movement behind a chimney.

I raise my hand. "Hold it, Lieutenant."

"Where?" he asks.

I point. He looks over my shoulder. "I'm not seeing anything."

I insist that he take cover and we both lean up against the side of a house. I am so sure there's a sniper lying in wait for us. After about two minutes, however, Lieutenant Gold straightens up, steps into the street and stands like a statue, as if offering himself as a target. I hold my breath. Nothing happens. The lieutenant takes another step and then, with more confidence, jogs ahead. Whatever I saw, it isn't shooting at us.

"Nerves getting the better of you?" he asks.

"I guess I'm tired, sir," I say.

We pass the remains of the first big barricade, the Flowerpot House and the spot where Jimmy died. It comes as a surprise to see how short the street is. In minutes we're back at the corner of Via Rapino. In a few minutes more we're at the square. And suddenly it's okay to stand up straight and stroll around. Piazza della Vittoria is securely in Canadian hands.

There's a troop of tanks lined up on one corner, 6-pounders on another. There are transport vehicles and Bren carriers and a regimental aid post under canvas near the little church where Loon threw the grenade that snuffed out the machine gun. For the first time in what seems a long time, I draw breath and exhale freely.

"Feels good to be out of it, doesn't it?" the lieutenant asks. I nod. "Make the most of it," he says. "It won't be for long."

I make my way to the mess tent and cadge a hard-boiled egg, fresh bread and a mug of tea. It's nothing much but it tastes wonderful.

I'm settling down to eat when I catch sight of Freddy Whitelaw. He waves, gets tea and then joins me. "You just had to drag us into this brawl, didn't you?" he says.

"Go on. You know you were getting bored. We did you a favour."

"Hear that?" he asks, waving a hand towards the east.

The guns we heard earlier, the 17-pounders, are still banging away from the edge of town.

"They've set them up on a headland and pointed them at the old town," he says. "They're blasting the buildings all along the edge of the esplanade and the railway yard below it. There's a tunnel down there that we think the Jerries have been using to move in supplies and reinforcements."

"So that's how they're getting fresh troops," I say. "Yesterday I saw a German up close. He was as fresh as a daisy."

"They don't have our supply-line problems," says Freddy. "We're still trucking munitions up from Foggia."

"How's D Company making out?" I gesture towards the Corso Vittorio Emanuele.

"They've made about as much progress as you have. They're at the foot of the Corso and are fighting to consolidate the square. It's been brutal."

"The fight for the square . . . "

"It's a killing ground. Machine guns, mortars, 88s. That's what I heard. The Jerries knocked the clock face out of the town hall to give them a machine-gun post."

"You've taken casualties?" I ask.

"We all have."

"You heard about Docherty?" He nods. "And the new man, Philpott?"

"Yeah. Other units have been hit just as hard," he says. "Or worse."

"And what about the Seaforths?"

"We're moving up your left flank," he says. "You'll see. We'll be at the castle before you."

"So it's a race?"

"To the death."

"You're funny," I say.

* * *

The lieutenant has company when he finds me again — a pair of sappers. Steve is a veteran with broad shoulders and big hands. Billy's scrawny. He has a habit of peering up at you from half-closed eyes. Steve, carrying standard-issue gear and not much else, bounces energetically on the balls of his feet. Billy's bent beneath a heavy backpack.

"You don't want to light a match near Billy," says Steve. "Or there'll be nothing left of you but smoke." Billy shifts his shoulder straps and winks.

"Got everything?" asks the lieutenant.

"Yessir," says Steve.

The rain has stopped but the sky is still the same colour as the cobblestones. We're careful again in making our way down Via Cespa. We hug the walls of houses and watch the windows and roofs. We hear the rattle and crack of small-arms fire and the rumble of artillery ahead of us and on either side, but nothing comes close. The Gaffer's watching for us through the open door of the last house, before the remains of the rubble barrier where Docherty died. He waves us in.

Paddy is keeping watch from the front room. The rest of the men — and Docherty's section too — are crammed into the kitchen, huddled around the stove. Lieutenant Gold takes the Gaffer into a corner of the kitchen. I catch fragments of their conversation.

"We need to make faster progress . . . " says the Gaffer.

"Vokes is pressuring Hoffy." This is the lieutenant talking. "The higher ups are putting pressure on Vokes."

The lieutenant again: "Any movement in the streets around here?"

The Gaffer says, "The men are holding up well . . . "

Finally, the lieutenant turns and addresses the rest of us. "Look here," he says. He pulls a map from a pocket inside his jacket and spreads it out on the kitchen table. We gather round as best we can.

"We're on this street," he says. "The Jerries blocked it off to hide their gun, but we're not at the end, not quite. We're at this cross street, Via Marconi. Cespa goes for another block and then ends at this larger street, Via Cavour."

"The Jerries have pulled back behind Marconi," says the Gaffer.

"There will be more traps," says the lieutenant. "Count on it."

The Gaffer nods. "More brawling."

"More street fighting," says Lieutenant Gold, "but with a difference. You'll see."

He grins and the rest of us looked mystified. The Gaffer frowns. I guess he isn't in on the secret.

"We'll cross Marconi now," says the lieutenant. "We'll take one more house on each side of Cespa. And then you'll see what we have in store."

Lieutenant Gold takes charge of Docherty's section, Lance Corporal Graham Turnbull taking Docherty's place. I know Turnbull as a quiet soldier with a pale push-broom moustache that he trims obsessively. Derrick calls him "the Walrus." He's a good guy, but needs to lose the moustache. You look at him and it's hard not to laugh.

"We'll go in without smoke," says the lieutenant. "The street is quiet and the light's fading. If we're quick and stay in the shadows, we'll take them by surprise."

"You think the Jerries have pulled back, sir?"

"They're regrouping for sure," says the lieutenant. "Smoke would just tell them we're coming."

"It's a bit chancy . . . " says the Gaffer.

"It's worth the risk," says Gold.

"Move quietly out there, you lot," says the Gaffer. "And mind your step. I'll shoot the first man who trips and makes a racket."

And so we set out, one section on each side of Via Cespa, each with its own objective. We leave behind the two sappers, with Specs to keep them company. They'll follow when the next house is secure.

The rain has stopped but the streets are wet. The stone surface shines dully under the grey evening sky. We're shadowy figures as we pick our way cautiously across the remains of the stone ramparts that were built around the now-shattered German gun. Nothing moves in the street ahead of us. No light shines from any window. The dark roofs blend into the clouds.

The tactic works. We're inside the next house in almost no time and Turnbull's unit gets the same result on the other side of the street. On our side, the Gaffer scours the premises while the rest of us wait in the corridor. He takes his time, letting his eyes become adjusted to the gloom. We know there's a trap somewhere. We're becoming accustomed to the Paras' ways. Still, I figure no one but the Gaffer would have found this device. It's in the front room, set to go off when someone sits on an upholstered chair.

"How the heck did you see *that*?" Doug asks him.

"Didn't look right," he answers. "The seat was high."

The Germans had placed a Teller mine under the cushion. Nothing could be simpler or more deadly. There would have been nothing left of anyone who sat on that chair. Nothing but blood and dust.

Paddy and Derrick have been checking out the upstairs rooms. They come bustling down just as Specs and the two sappers trot in, having been given the all-clear signal.

"There's Jerries next door," Derrick hisses. "We heard them through the wall."

"Jeez," says Loon. "If we can hear *them* . . . "

"Keep your voices down!"

The Gaffer gestures for me to follow him as he makes his way to the front door. "Be ready," he says.

I take up a position that gives me a broad view of the street. The Gaffer waves his hand and I see movement in the house opposite. And then, wasting no time, the lieutenant emerges from the doorway opposite and runs, crouching, towards us. He just makes it.

The enemy wakes up. His bullets tear holes in the door frame. I roll over and back without shooting. I move back along the corridor to where the others are clustered.

"They've got us where they want us now, haven't they?" says Doug softly.

The lieutenant says, "We'll see about that."

But it's obvious we're in a jam. The Germans know these streets and buildings. They occupied this house just hours before us. At any moment they could charge down the street and toss in a potato masher or mount a more organized attack. And yet, because their machine guns and rifles are already lined up and in position, we hardly dare to poke a nose out the door.

Derrick is wearing a hunted look. Paddy claps a hand on his shoulder. "Nothing to worry about," he says.

"Where are the sappers?" asks the lieutenant.

The grizzled one, Steve, bounces forward. "Here, Lieutenant." Billy slopes up behind him. I'm beginning to think his habit of winking is a nervous tic.

"The sappers call it mouse-holing," says the lieutenant. "Tell them about it, Corporal."

Steve steps up. "It's simple, Lieutenant. We blow a hole in the wall between the houses. You know, the shared wall. Then we get out of the way and you go through, shooting."

The Gaffer's looking at the pair intently. "Through the *wall*," he says.

"Yessir," says Steve.

"B Company's been doing it," says the lieutenant. "You see the advantage . . . "

"Yessir, I believe I do."

"You don't have to show yourself in the street," says the lieutenant. "And the element of surprise . . . "

"Suddenly the wall explodes . . . " says the Gaffer, a smile forming on his lips.

"Hard for the Jerries to prepare for an attack like that," mutters Paddy.

"Jeez," says Loon. "Why didn't we think of it sooner?"

"Shut it, Private Crawford," says the lieutenant, surprising us by using Loon's last name. "Be glad we thought of it at all."

* * *

It's almost as easy as Steve had said it would be. We wait either on or at the foot of the staircase while the two sappers set a charge against the common wall in an upstairs room. They lean a chair against the explosive to hold it in place. Then they unspool the fuse and back up to the stairs. Those of us near the top cover our ears with our hands. Those at the bottom keep an eye on the door. Paddy's last in line. He's standing as if on sentry duty, which in a way he is.

KABOOM!

Even with my ears covered, the noise of the explosion inside that enclosed space is terrific. It shakes the walls and the woodwork. It shakes my bones and my guts. A cloud of dust sweeps over us. We leap up, Loon first with a hand grenade, and then Doug with the Sten gun, and then the rest of us. We dash forward, ready for action as the dirty mist settles around our feet . . . and then we stop.

There's a hole, all right. It's just big enough for a man to crawl through. But it's a hole in one wall only — and there are two. A double wall! The sappers, sensing something is wrong, step up behind us. One glance tells them what has to be done.

"Don't worry about a thing," says Steve. "We'll soon have that fixed." And they repeat the performance. They have to do it without the chair, which now is in splinters. They find and use a small table instead. We take our places.

KABOOM!

It's as loud as before. It sends the same shock wave over and through us. Loon takes the lead. Doug is close behind him. Loon tosses a grenade through the hole. When it explodes, Doug dives through the hole, with me right behind him. I stumble and almost fall, then find my feet again. Doug sprays the room with bullets. I see one, two . . . three crumpled figures on the floor. I hear moaning and crying. Loon, at the head of the stairs, tosses another grenade. I hear it bounce on the wooden steps. Another explosion. We scramble down to the ground floor and find one motionless body and two wounded Germans who offer no resistance. One, his face bloodied and his tunic torn, squirms like a fish on the hook. The other lifts shaking hands in the air.

We stop at the foot of the stairs and look at one another. The whole operation has taken about ninety seconds.

"That was something," says Loon.

Strong John makes a move to disarm the Germans.

Derrick glances around, suddenly alarmed. "Where's Paddy?" he says.

"What?"

"Where's my brother?"

He turns and bounds back up the stairs. I follow close behind him. The pounding of our boots echoes off the walls. Derrick throws himself through the tunnel that now connects the two houses. "Paddy! I'm coming!"

"Watch it, Derrick!" I shout. The Gaffer is behind me. He's yelling too. "Heads up, Derrick! You don't know . . . "

But Derrick does know. They're brothers, after all. Derrick sees it all in his head before we get to the bottom of the stairs.

Paddy is still alive. His head is jammed between the bottom step and the wall. He's grimacing in pain. His teeth shine in the gloom and his eyes are squeezed shut. He has one hand pressed tightly against his chest. With the other he pounds on the floor. A glistening pool, black in the darkened hallway, seeps from his side across the floor.

"Medic!" Derrick screams the word.

"We need a runner," says the Gaffer. "Doug!"

Derrick is kneeling beside his brother, cradling Paddy's head in his hands. "Paddy, what happened?"

I glance through the open door into the street. There's another body crumpled on the cobblestones. Another German. They must have launched an attack behind us. The German and Paddy must have confronted each other as we were scrambling up the stairs.

Doug stops for a second to examine the body in the street. Then he runs to get help.

Derrick stays with the stretcher bearers when they take Paddy back to the aid post. The Gaffer's reluctant to see him go. We're badly under strength already. We can hardly afford the loss of another man, but he couldn't in all conscience order Derrick to stay. Derrick would have disobeyed the order anyway.

We mouse-hole our way into the next building. The Germans are better prepared for us this time — they pull out fast after the explosion.

Surprisingly, they clear out of the house across the street too. By evening we're in sole possession of Via Cespa. From an upstairs window in the last house, we have a view over the cross street, Via Cavour. We would celebrate our victory if it weren't for what we've lost.

* * *

A decent dinner, thanks to the quartermaster's crew, now that the street is safe. We heat up stew that actually looks like something I might have eaten at home. Half the unit eats and naps while the other half watches the intersection from different vantage points. There is occasional excitement. At least one enemy sniper is at work in the neighbourhood and there are signs of movement. We hear the roar of engines, and shouted orders, as well as the usual crackle and rumble of battle. Some comes from our side, some from the other. It's hard to tell.

While we're taking turns to rest, Lieutenant Gold and the Gaffer put their heads together again. I listen in as they talk things over. The losses we've taken worry them. Our section is down to six men — counting Derrick, who's still with his brother. Turnbull's section is down to six too. If we put the two together, we have only one full-strength section. Boss Chudleigh's section, operating on the next street, isn't much better off. But then, the whole battalion is operating at half-strength or less.

"Funny thing is," says the lieutenant. "For this type of fighting, small groups may be better than big ones."

The Gaffer nods his head. "Faster and more flexible. We've done okay in the house-to-house battles."

"But overall, our progress is slow. The Jerries have more firepower."

"When do you reckon we can call up the tanks?"

"Maybe sooner rather than later," says the lieutenant. "D Company is working now with a troop of Three Rivers Tanks to secure Piazza Municipale."

"Major Stone and the tank corps have come to an understanding then?" says the Gaffer.

"Stone's a determined man."

"And the Corso is clear?"

The lieutenant nods.

"I wouldn't want to have been that tank chap," says the Gaffer.

The lieutenant smiles. "He's very sorry, I'm sure."

Captain Trehan turns up after we've eaten. He has an intelligence officer from the Three Rivers Regiment with him. The lieutenant and the Gaffer order the rest of us out of the kitchen — and away from the warm stove — so the officers can use the table.

Later, after the captain and the intelligence officer leave, we find out from the lieutenant what the visit means.

"We're here on Via Cavour," he says, stabbing the middle of the map. Piazza Municipale, the biggest of the town squares, is to the east of us. B and D companies are in the process of securing it and are moving past it, along the esplanade, which overlooks the port, to the castle. There's another, smaller square to the west of us, Piazza San Francesco, where there's another church and a school. The Germans have established machine-gun positions in the church tower and around the square. Our job is to eliminate them."

"Where are the Seaforths?" I ask. From what Freddy Whitelaw told me, I thought the Highlanders had taken over the west side.

"They're on the other side of the church square," says the lieutenant. "The enemy has a firm base in a cemetery in the northwest corner of town — "

"That will be handy when the time comes," says Loon.

" . . . and in the castle on the northeast corner. They're getting supplies from the north, using the gully on that side and the railway tunnel as cover. The Seaforths are driving through the west side of the old town towards the cemetery, with the intention, ultimately, of cutting off the German supply line to the north."

"So, our orders . . . " says the Gaffer.

"Our orders are to proceed along Via Cavour towards Piazza San Francesco. We can expect to meet resistance. Once we get there, we'll do whatever is necessary to neutralize the enemy machine guns and consolidate the square. Now, is everything clear?"

The men mostly grunt in reply.

"We'll stay put this evening," says the lieutenant, "and move in the morning. Get some rest while you can."

* * *

Derrick's back. I'm keeping watch from the front room when he wanders past the window. He doesn't respond when I challenge him. I might have shot him, but I can make out his shape and the way he walks and, anyway, I'm half-expecting him.

"Hell, Derrick," I say when I open the door. "You've got to answer when you're asked for the password."

"What's the password?" he says. "I forget."

His chunky face is tight and drawn. He looks worn out.

"How's Paddy?" I ask.

He shakes his head. "Not good."

The Gaffer joins us. He puts a hand on Derrick's shoulder. "They've taken him to San Vito Chietino?" he asks. There's a field hospital there.

"Yes," says Derrick.

"So his condition is stable?"

"He's barely conscious," says Derrick. "He'd open his eyes and try to say something. He knew I was there . . . "

"Well, that's something."

"He said to tell Ma and Pa he loves them. And his girl."

"That's good . . . "

"It's what men say when they're *dying*."

"It's what they say when they're *hurt*," I say. "It doesn't mean he's dying."

"I can't imagine him gone," says Derrick. "He's always been there. We looked out for one another."

"He'll be back," I say.

Derrick shakes his head and says, "I don't think so."

"Derrick . . . " says the Gaffer, but Derrick isn't paying attention. He looks at us with a baffled expression.

"I was so sure it was going to be me."

Chapter 9
Dead Horse Square
Friday, December 24

It's cold and dark when Doug nudges me with his boot. "We have a visitor," he says. He gestures towards the door.

"Who?"

"You'll see."

I haul myself to my feet, rub my hands together for warmth and flex my toes. I make my way past the other guys spread out around the room. Some are snoring, others are restless, their faces lined and their eyes ringed with dark shadows. At first I see only Specs in the hallway. He's sitting on the stairs, his rifle resting on his knees. Following his glance, I see her. Teresa, with her jet black hair and oval face, is standing just inside the door.

She doesn't say hello or explain how she found me or how she got here. She says simply, "Por favore, venga con me." *Please come with me.*

"Where to?"

"Just come."

It isn't so much her voice that catches my

attention, though there is urgency in her tone. It's her eyes that convince me. I go back to the living room to gather up my rifle and backpack. I step carefully around the other men and their belongings, making as little noise as I can. The Gaffer, stretched out in a corner, never stirs.

Doug is by the door, watching me. "You're going with her?" he says.

"Yes," I answer.

He blinks and says, "You're nuts." I guess he's right. If I'm not back before they miss me, I could be charged for leaving my unit. But we're so short of men now, and the situation is so tense, I don't think the Gaffer will do anything but bawl me out. He needs us here.

No lights shine from the windows on Via Cavour. The low clouds reflect the flash of artillery in the east. The dull irregular glow casts sudden shadows along the fronts of houses. These are more uneven than the ones on Via Cespa, making more shadows for us — and the Jerries — to hide in. Teresa tugs at my sleeve and, hugging the nearside wall, leads me west towards what the lieutenant said was another square. One occupied by the Germans.

But then we turn north, up an alley. Teresa stops in a doorway and points at a building up the way.

"Tedeschi," she says. *Germans.*

She pushes open a door and leads me inside a building so dark that I might as well be blind. With her hand on my sleeve, she takes me downstairs and then up again into a tiny courtyard and another building. By now I've lost all sense of where we are or where we're headed.

We dash across another alley. We creep past houses that are occupied, where we hear low voices, and we stop to peer from windows as enemy soldiers trudge by. We meet a man in a basement who nods at me as he whispers in Teresa's ear.

"Stanno muovendosi," she says. *They are moving.* The Germans, they are bringing in more men.

I ask her where. She says, the cemetery. So the Germans are planning a counterattack. This is not surprising. It would be surprising if they weren't.

And then she leads me once more into alleys, gardens and houses, some untouched and others wrecked, until finally we come to a stop. "Aspettiamo qui," she says. *We'll wait here.*

We're in a house that the Germans have partly demolished. The front wall has been reduced to rubble. The stones and timber have been pushed into the street. But an inner wall is still standing and the room behind it is untouched.

There's a table and chairs, and cupboards above and below the counter. There's a pitcher full of water, and a cup.

We wait in the strange wreck of a house. There are walls around us, but no ceiling, just stars. I ask after Claudia and her little boy.

"Non lo so," she says. *I don't know.* She shrugs and says she'll find out more tonight.

She's quiet for a moment. Then she asks me where I'm from. I start to explain that I'm from western Canada, from Alberta, but she looks at me without understanding. What part of Italy is what she wants to know. "I miei genitori vengono dal sud," I say finally. *My parents are from the south.* "And you?"

"Io sono di qui." *I'm from here, from Ortona. My family has lived here, or in the country around here forever. From the beginning.*

I ask her what her family does.

"My father and uncle own land. Some they farm. Some they rent to others."

We're sitting close to one another. I can feel the warmth of her skin. I put my arm around her shoulders.

A shape appears without warning at the door. Teresa stands up quickly as a woman dressed in black — a nun — sweeps into the room. She and

Teresa hold each others' hands for a moment and then Teresa introduces me.

"Sorella Domenica, vorrei farle conoscere Paolo, un soldato canadese."

I give Sister Domenica my chair. Teresa tells me she has just come from the hospital.

The sister speaks fast, even more quickly than Teresa, and I have trouble understanding her. Teresa has to help me, and soon she simply repeats more slowly — still in Italian — what the nun has to say: There are more than one hundred people in the hospital. Many are from the town and have taken refuge there. Not just sick people, but also people who have lost their homes. They have nowhere to go.

I nod that I understand. She goes on. The hospital is next to the church on the square, Piazza San Francesco. The Germans are in the church and school as well as the hospital.

"Is there a machine gun there?" I ask.

"She says yes, in the church tower, but not in the hospital. Just soldiers are in the hospital," Teresa tells me. "But conditions are very bad. They have no food, no medicine. The bathrooms are not clean. There are too many people."

"The Germans aren't helping?"

"The Germans have given them nothing."

"They have to get out of there," I say.

Teresa and the sister talk some more, then Teresa tells me that the nuns intend to lead the people in the hospital to safety. She wants to take them to us, to the Canadians.

"You say there are more than *one hundred*?"

She explains that there are eight Germans in the hospital. Sometimes more, sometimes less, but they don't all agree. Some want to let our people go. Others are against it. They think it's a trick, that the Canadians will use the people as a shield to cover an attack.

"But the *Germans* are using the people as a shield," I say. "Holding them hostage?"

"Si," says Teresa, they are hostages. Neither she nor the sister speaks for a moment. Then Sister Domenica says the people can't stay in the hospital. They will die. She intends to lead them out tomorrow no matter what the Germans say. And then Teresa adds, "Claudia's in the hospital. She is weak. Her son is in there too."

* * *

Dawn is happening somewhere on the far side of the clouds when we start back. Teresa takes me by a different route from the one we followed before. She wants me to see the square where the hospital is. So she leads me to a block of buildings on the eastern side of the piazza. Then, instead of threading our way through basements and courtyards, she takes me up two flights of stairs and up a rickety ladder to an attic, and from there, through a window and onto the roof.

We scramble to the peak and suddenly I glimpse what the snipers get to see — the town is at my feet. Light from the cloud-filtered sun casts a dull glow over the buildings. To the north, on a height of land, there's the splintered tower of Cathedrale San Tommaso. Sloping below it is a tangle of alleys that lead to the main square. The town hall, the most massive building on the square, looks south to where we've come from. To our west, just a block away, there's another tower. Teresa, seeing where I'm looking, gestures towards it.

"Chiesa di San Francesco," she says. *The church of Saint Francis.*

"And the hospital?"

She points past it. I take it that the hospital is beside it, over there.

With morning comes noise. Engines are started, orders are shouted, riflemen take potshots at targets we can't see. The roof slopes gently to the gutter, but it's slippery with dew. I flip over onto my back and dig into my pockets. Teresa bites into the chocolate I give her as if it were something new, something she's never tried.

"From Canada?" she asks.

"It comes from England," I tell her. "Eighth Army issue. It's made from mud, bugs and the blood of ferrets."

"Cosa intendi?" *What?*

"A joke."

She nods and then says, "Via Cavour is that way. Where your friends are."

"We should go."

We stay on the rooftops, scrambling carefully from one to another, stopping from time to time to look around. We come to a point where we have to climb down again, to cross an alley, but she leads me into another building with stairs, a window and a roof.

"E l'alba," she says. *Now it's light.* "Up here we can see the enemy before he sees us."

Slowly, by crossing one roof after another, we move closer to the corner of Cespa and Cavour. Together we peer over the peak at the houses on the other side. We're too high up and the angle is too steep for us to see more than a narrow strip of the street. A soldier leans out of a second-floor window. The red patch on his shoulder marks him as Canadian. I open my mouth, meaning to identify myself.

A shot rings out. A soldier — a Canadian by the sound of it — lets out a yell. One of our guys has been hit. Suddenly the air is full of the noise of rifle and machine-gun fire. Teresa clutches my arm. I reach for my weapon. She asks what I'm doing. I don't answer. I start wriggling across the tile roof so I can see more of what's happening down below. A hand grenade explodes inside a building, and then another. More small-arms fire and then . . . silence.

I make it as far as the gutter, in time to see one of our men roll a smoke canister onto the pavement. I glimpse the crown of a Canadian helmet. And then the familiar, awkward shape of Loon emerges from the haze. It would be Loon! He's shinnying up another drainpipe, reaching for the balcony. Below him there's another soldier — Specs! Loon reaches for the balcony railing. A glass-paned door opens from the house onto the balcony. Something moves behind it. I pull the butt of the rifle against my shoulder, aim and squeeze the trigger . . .

CRACK!

"Fai attenzione!" It's Teresa.

A black-clad figure shoots from the roof across the street. A clay tile explodes not 6 inches from my hip. I aim again and fire.

CRACK!

The German sniper falls forward. His rifle slides from his hands, skates across the tiles and tumbles from the roof to the ground.

* * *

The lieutenant looks really annoyed when I introduce him to Teresa. He doesn't want to hear about the hostages.

"There's nothing I can do if I'm nowhere near the square," he says.

"La posso portare io l portare io lì," says Teresa. *I can take you there.*

"What do you mean?" says the lieutenant when I translate.

She goes to a window — we're in the house that Turnbull's section seized from the Germans. She points across the street to the house occupied by the Gaffer's crew.

"Da dove sono . . . " she says. I translate her words for the lieutenant: "From where they are, you can go most of the distance to Piazza San Francesco. You can make your holes in the walls . . . "

Now I know what she means: mouse holes. She can show us where to make mouse holes. Along Via Cavour and Marconi, where they meet at the corner of the square.

Lieutenant Gold is quietly furious with me.

I can tell by the way he glances at me and then looks away. He has no time to deal with privates who wander off in the night and then return with civilians. It doesn't help that he thinks all Italians are traitors. Or if not traitors, then unreliable. Maybe he thinks that about me too. But still, he mulls over Teresa's offer, drums his fingers on the windowsill and finally says, "Okay."

With smoke and some fireworks to cover our movements, we cross Cavour and join the Gaffer's crew. The Gaffer glares at me, no happier with me than the lieutenant, but he says nothing. Some of the others cast admiring glances at Teresa. Later, I have a few words with Doug. He tells me the German sniper got one of Turnbull's men before I got the sniper.

"How's he doing?" I ask.

"Banged up, but he'll live. He was struck in the shoulder."

"And Loon?"

"See for yourself. He thinks he's invincible."

Loon is leaning back on a wooden chair, his feet resting on a table. He has a big grin on his face.

Meanwhile, Lieutenant Gold and the Gaffer put their heads together. The lieutenant looks at me and I look at Teresa.

"Di qua," she says. *This way.*

* * *

With Teresa to show us the way, our two sections start blasting an inside path to Piazza San Francesco. I lose count of the number of explosions and firefights, and the number of grenades that are thrown. There are times when the Germans seem to know we're coming. At no point are they taken entirely by surprise. We have the sense that they're trying to come up with tactics to counter our hole-through-the-wall attacks. More than once we're met with a quick assault after our first grenades are tossed through the hole. But only we know when we're going to make a move. Only we know what floor we're going to strike on. Sometimes we start on the top floor and work our way down. Other times, if we know they're concentrated on the ground floor, we go in that way and then work our way up. We have them at a disadvantage. And we're moving fast.

There are a few opportunities to gossip. We crack bad jokes when we're crouching on staircases, waiting for the sappers to set a charge.

"Where there's a wall, there's a way."

"This business is changing Turnbull. Just look at his beady eyes, twitching nose and whiskers."

"Especially the whiskers."

"When this is over, I'm coming back to Ortona as a plasterer."

"So basically we're making business for you."

"Exactly."

"You're welcome."

Sometime around mid-morning, the lieutenant, satisfied that we're making progress, leaves us to get on with it. Soon after that, Teresa speaks to me.

"Devo lasciare," she says. *I have to leave.*

We're close to the corner now. We no longer need her guidance. Her hand touches mine as she departs and it's like a spark passes between us.

We suffer no serious casualties. As far as we can tell, the enemy isn't hurt badly either. In any event, they leave no bodies behind. But they are giving up territory, bit by bit. At around 1100 hours we cross Marconi. A half hour later we take over the last building before the square. In the house across the street, on the southwest corner, there's movement behind the windows. The Gaffer takes a look.

"They're ours," he says. "It's Boss Chudleigh's section. The lieutenant's with them." Then he adds, "He's coming over."

We make the usual preparations, provide what cover we can. We get a surprise when an enemy machine gun opens up. They have a post at the far end of the alley across from us. Lieutenant Gold throws himself through the open door, lands in a heap on the floor and scrambles to his feet before anyone can help him. His expression is rueful.

"Not the way Monty would have done it," he says.

The map comes out and we gather round.

"When you look north out the window," he says, "you can see partway up an alley leading to this intersection, here." He stabs the map with his finger. "The enemy has a heavy machine gun at the end of the alley. I personally saw evidence that it's there when I crossed the street.

"On the other side of the alley from where we are now, there's the back side of a school. The front of the school overlooks Piazza San Francesco. We know there's German troops in there. Across from the school is the church. They have a machine gun in the tower. Beside the church there's a hospital. We're told there are civilians inside. To take control of the square, we have to neutralize the German position in the church tower. To do that, we first have to seize the school. So that's what we're going to do now."

"More smoke, shoot and frag?" says Loon. This, after all, is the way we've been fighting for what seems like days.

"B and D companies have consolidated around the main square, Piazza Municipale," says the lieutenant. "We have the beginnings of a firm base in the centre of the town. Now we can take the fight to the enemy properly."

"Tanks," says the Gaffer. He's smiling.

The lieutenant smiles too. "Damn right, there'll be tanks," he says. We think the enemy is defending the front of the school where it looks out over the square. That's where the main door is and where his guns are pointing. There is no door in the end of the school, the end nearest us. There's just a wall.

"We're bringing up a troop of tanks. Their first assignment is to blast through that wall. There isn't a door there now, but there will be when they're finished. You, gentlemen, will enter the school by way of the new door. Understood?"

* * *

"Just look at that gorgeous hunk of metal!" says Loon as the first Sherman rumbles up Via Cavour. "I could run out and kiss its filthy flanks."

"Nothing's stopping you," I say. Loon jumps up as if he means to do it and Strong John reaches out as if he means to stop him. There's no denying that we're thrilled. The Lee-Enfield .303 is a useful weapon and the Sten sub-machine gun is the last word in hand-held mayhem, but there's something about a 75-mm cannon mounted on an armoured chassis with built-in machine guns and the capacity to roll unstoppably at 25 or 30 miles per hour that fills a rifleman with joy. We peer from the windows as the tanks move into position. The lead machine stops in front of us on Via Cavour. The other two hang back half a block behind it. We watch as the leader's turret turns towards the school. The cannon's elevation drops a few degrees. There's a pause. I imagine the tank commander peering through his periscope, checking in with the gunner and then giving the order to fire.

BOOM!

A piece of the wall comes down in a flurry of dust.

BOOM!

The hole gets bigger. The cannon's angle is lifted a titch.

BOOM!

With each shot, the cloud of dust expands and the pile of masonry gets bigger.

BOOM!

The tank is taking fire from across the square. Enemy machine-gunners in the church tower have it in their sights. The tank's own machine guns are giving back as good as they get, or better. The Sherman's armour is tough enough to take the hate that's being hurled at it. And more of the school crumbles under the cannon's battering assault.

BOOM!

"When do we move in, Sergeant?" asks Loon.

The Gaffer says, "Wait."

The lead tank's turret turns again so the cannon points towards the square. Somewhere inside the Sherman's interior the driver shifts into gear. It lurches forward, rumbles past the corner of the school and then stops. The other two tanks grind forward too, one taking up a position beside the lead tank and the other settling down at the intersection with the alley. Again there's a pause while the tank crews size up their targets.

BOOM! BOOM! BOOM!

The three Shermans open fire all at once. The two in front work over the church, the third takes aim at the machine-gun nest that almost did in Lieutenant Gold

BOOM! BOOM! BOOM!

Stones are flying in all directions as bits of buildings came apart. The dust rises up like marsh mist, so that the outlines of structures are obscured.

The Gaffer raises his hand. "Get ready!" he says.

We form up, our weapons at the ready.

"Go!"

We file out one after the other, first Derrick and then Strong John and Loon with the Bren gun, then Doug and I and Specs and the Gaffer bringing up the rear.

BOOM! BOOM! BOOM!

The tanks keep on shooting. Amid the noise and confusion it's impossible to tell apart the sound of enemy and friendly guns. Is the enemy even shooting back? We jog across the rubble-covered street. The ground shakes beneath us in time with the guns. With the noise, the vibrations and the swirling dirt that makes it hard to see, my head is spinning. But then the grey mass of the school appears in front of me. I see Strong John and Loon leap onto the pile of wrecked wood and masonry. They scramble through the opening. I leap, lose my footing and then recover. I'm in.

We're at the end of a long corridor. Derrick, in front, pulls the pin from a 36, kicks down the first door he comes to and tosses the grenade inside. He leans back until it explodes and then plunges into the cloud he has stirred up. Strong John and Loon take up a position to cover the corridor while Doug and I glance into Derrick's room to make sure it's free of enemy soldiers. Then we move on. One room, two rooms, three rooms are clear. I run for the next one with Doug on my heels.

"Look out!"

The second Loon calls out his warning, we come under fire. Three Germans are shooting wildly in our direction. In an instant Strong John is prone, the Bren on its tripod, spewing murder. The rest of us take shelter in doorways. Doug leans out and fires a burst from the Sten gun. He steps back and I take his place, but I'm way off-target. It's impossible to take aim without drawing fire. But Strong John is vulnerable. I have to do something.

I reach into my webbing for a hand grenade, pull the pin and, grasping the door frame with my free hand, use it as a pivot to swing into the hall. The grenade caroms off the floor and the walls like a pinball. The Germans yell and take cover. The grenade explodes and the noise shakes the school.

"I'm moving!" Doug yells the warning to keep the rest of us from shooting. He springs from the doorway where he's been sheltering, fires once at the enemy and then runs for the next room on the other side. At that moment, something solid slides rapidly towards us. A potato masher. Doug sees it coming, grabs and hurls it back to where it came from and tumbles into another room. The German bomb blows up before it reaches them. Loon pops out from his doorway and rolls another grenade at the Germans. I follow with yet another one. We're in a bowling alley with bombs instead of balls.

Two Germans are down. The third has disappeared.

"Moving!"

Loon moves up and then I do the same. Into every room we reach, we throw a hand grenade. After every blast, we run in shooting. Room after room is empty. Ahead of us there's an open space, which has to be the foyer and, around the corner, the front door.

"Running low on 36s," says Loon suddenly. I am too.

The Gaffer slides an ammunition pouch forward. Taking turns, we replenish our supply.

"Moving!"

It's Doug's turn. He dekes around the body of one of the two Germans, ducks into another classroom and repeats the frag-and-shoot routine. We're getting close to the front entrance. This is where the machine gun is positioned, pointing at the square. Doug re-emerges from the classroom, points to the corner and glances my way. I hold up a 36. He nods his head in agreement. I dash to the corner and then slide past the foyer, letting go of the grenade as I whizz by. It tumbles and rolls towards the wall on the other side of the opening.

Loon comes up behind me and sends another one in the same direction. They explode, one after the other. I pick myself up, turn and dash back again, hurling myself across the floor as if it's the World Series and I'm headed for home plate. As I come to a stop, I fire another two rounds from my rifle at the doors. Glass shatters. Wood splinters. I pause to assess what I've achieved. Most of the damage was done before I got there. The doors are gone and so is much of the outside wall. Rubble ramparts protected the German gun, which has been abandoned. There's no sign of the gun's crew. I draw a deep breath.

The Gaffer saunters up behind me.

"Nice slide, Paul," he says. "I didn't know you played baseball."

I'm still on the floor. The Gaffer is standing over me. He's soon joined by Strong John, Loon and the others. They stand around me for a minute, looking amused and superior. I haul myself up and brush the dust off my pants.

"Fine," I say. "I took this one. The next machine-gun nest is yours."

* * *

It looks like the Germans have high-tailed it, but we take the time to make sure. We work our way to the end of the building, opening doors, turning over furniture, poking in cupboards. Not an enemy soldier is found.

We look in the basement too. What we discover there is a great big pile of ammunition — all kinds — artillery shells, mortar bombs, the works.

"Looks like they meant to stay for a while," says Doug.

Sure now that the school is clear, we gather around what's left of the German machine gun and gaze out at the square. The tanks have moved closer to the church with Chudleigh's section advancing behind them. There's sporadic fire coming from a low building across the way.

"We should be turning the tanks on that," says Loon.

"Can't," says the Gaffer.

"It's the hospital," I say. "There's civilians in there."

"You mean they're hiding behind *civilians*?" says Loon.

As we stand there watching, I notice something moving in the northwest corner of the square. A dun-coloured horse emerges from a side street. It's moving at a trot, sometimes breaking into a canter. It's obviously agitated, uncertain which way to turn. It makes its way, stopping and starting, to the centre of the piazza, and stands there for a moment, shaking its head and flicking its tail. A man appears from the same street, a little man wearing a narrow-brimmed hat and a dark brown jacket. He's waving his arms. I can't hear what he's saying, but it's obvious he's calling to the horse. The horse doesn't hear him or, if it does, it's too rattled to pay attention. It tosses its head as if coming to a decision, turns south and then breaks into a gallop.

"Go, horse, go!" says Loon quietly beside me.

I can't tell for sure where the shots come from, but I suspect it's from our guys, now in the church. The horse goes down. Its legs churn the air briefly. It lifts its head up once, twice, and then lies still.

"Aw, hell," says Loon.

* * *

The taking of Dead Horse Square — what everyone calls it now — feels like some kind of turning point. For days, we've been fighting in small units, feeling our way forward as if stuck in a fog. Often, there really is a fog — an early morning mist or evening veil of rain. Or the fog we make ourselves, made up of dust, smoke and the stuff thrown up by high explosives. And then there's the fog that fills our heads, the fog of not knowing where our buddies are or what the enemy is doing.

The weather hasn't exactly made it easier to see

what's ahead. The cloud cover has been constant, sometimes heavier and blacker, sometimes lighter, but not once this week have we seen the sun. Our planes have been grounded because of it. All the advantages have been with the enemy. He chose where to make a stand. He prepared his defences, set up fields of fire and planted booby traps. He pulled back when it suited him. He held all the best cards.

The lieutenant says you need three attacking soldiers for every defender to overcome the advantage enjoyed by men fighting from a fixed position. I'm pretty sure the Germans outnumber us. At best we're about even. And they're good soldiers, the Germans. They're Hitler's true believers.

Nothing prepared us for this. We've had to figure out how to survive and win one house at a time. For the most part, we've done it without tanks, field guns or mortars. And when tanks were involved, they've mostly followed the infantry instead fighting beside us. Our 6-pounders have been used against buildings more often than against tanks. We've usually been too close to the enemy to bring in mortars. The battle has been fought by the foot-sloggers. That's us. We've done it with our rifles and sub-machine guns. We've done it with hand grenades. We've done it with our hands.

This evening — it's Christmas Eve! — we've taken over another part of town, to the east of Dead Horse Square. D Company has occupied the main square. They're in position to push the Germans out of the winding streets and narrow alleys of the old town below the cathedral and, beyond it, the castle. And it's different now. The Three Rivers Tanks are in position to lead the way around the esplanade that overlooks the port. Our artillery has found where the enemy is concentrated and is banging away at it. The enemy is getting no more rest than we are. We're in a position to link up with other units and move in together to finish them off. We can finally, as the Gaffer puts it, start acting like an army again.

* * *

Captain Trehan is here. He met with the lieutenant first and then stopped by each section. He's less formal than usual, and looks and sounds worn out.

"I could not be more proud of you," he says at last. "You're a credit to the regiment. Canada's proud of you. Well done."

No one says anything.

"Of course," he adds, "it's not over yet."

"We're in touch with the Seaforths," says the lieutenant after the captain has left. They're pushing along the outside edge of town. We'll move beside them, but on the inside, closer to the centre. Their main axis is Via Monte Maiella." He points to the map that's tacked to the schoolroom wall. "It leads to another square, Piazza Plebiscito . . . "

"Another darn square," says Loon.

"It's not much of a square," says the lieutenant. "More like an intersection where a number of streets meet. But it won't be easy to take. It's at the base of the hill where the cathedral is situated. The enemy has the high ground."

"Like always," says Loon.

I nudge him. "You're getting awfully mouthy there, pal."

"Uh huh," he says.

"But this time we won't go in alone," the lieutenant continues. "When we reach the square, we'll be in position to bring up a troop of Three Rivers Tanks. The mortar platoon is available too, to tackle the high ground. We'll make use of our firepower now that we have more room to move.

"I'm not saying it's going to be easy," he adds, "but it should be easier than it has been. Any questions?"

"What about the hospital?" I ask him. "There are still Jerries there?"

"The Seaforths have it staked out," says the lieutenant.

"Are we bypassing it, sir?"

"That's correct. They'll have to give themselves up eventually."

There are no other questions.

Doug looks at me curiously. "What about the hospital?" he asks.

I say, "Claudia's there."

* * *

At dusk we move out of the school and work with the other two sections to secure a base in one of the streets, Via Ciampoli, behind it. Our objective is a corner café. In our hearts we know better, but we can't help hoping there's something left on the shelves. Doug started it. He said, "What if there's a nice piece of meat in the icebox? A veal cutlet maybe?" That's all it took to get us all dreaming. We've been eating Compo rations for so long, it's hard to remember what real food tastes like.

We turf out the Germans after a brief struggle. In fact, they pull back so fast that it makes us suspicious. The Gaffer is especially careful when he goes looking for booby traps. He's got the right idea. He finds a German pistol on a stool behind the counter. Just about everyone wants a German Luger. You can sell them for a fortune behind the lines. I guess the Germans know this: the Luger on the stool has a fishing line attached to it. The line leads to an explosive under the seat.

"That would have been the last souvenir some sap picked up," says the Gaffer.

He finds another charge planted in the toilet, set to explode as soon as someone sat on the throne. "And that would cure your constipation," he observes. "Permanently."

There's yet another charge set to explode when someone sets foot on the bottom step of the staircase that leads from the back of the café to the rooms upstairs.

"Bloody Hell!" says the Gaffer when he uncovers it. "There's enough high explosive here to bring the whole building down."

As for food, there are dirty plates and bowls piled neatly on a table. A carefully lettered note, written in English, has been left on the counter: *VERY DELICIOUS SOUP. SORRY, CANADA. ALL GONE.*

When, at last, the Gaffer is satisfied that he has found every last one of the enemy's nasty surprises, and the rest of us are convinced that the enemy has really taken every morsel of food, we post sentries and settle down for the night. It's not quiet. For sure there are Germans farther up the street. Shots ring out as snipers sneak around the neighbourhood, watching for the flutter of a curtain or the glow of a cigarette. Occasionally a machine gun barks in the darkness. They're meant to keep us awake and scared.

"What happened last night?" Doug asks me.

"Last night?"

"When you went off with Teresa."

"Oh, that." It seems like such a long time ago.

"Yes, that."

"There are so many people in this town," I tell him. "It's as if the town we're fighting in sits on top of another, underground town."

"You mean the civilians?"

"Yeah. Lots of them left, but just as many seem to have stayed behind. They have nowhere to go now. And no way to travel. Hardly any mules or carts. Vehicles are out of the question. The Jerries requisitioned everything. The trains . . . "

"Not like it was before the war," says Doug.

He's right. Mussolini was famous for making the trains run on time. It was regarded as Fascism's greatest achievement. The trains were the glory of the Fascist state.

"It's mostly old people who've been left behind," I say. "The ones who can't walk far. But also women with children. And children who've lost their parents. The orphans. They're in cellars, back rooms and attics. Everywhere."

Doug is no longer listening. There's something else on his mind. "Teresa is really something," he says.

"I don't know how she manages it, but she's all over the town," I tell him. "Bringing people together, searching for food. People are starving. She showed me things, where the Jerries are. She wants us to know she's on our side."

We're lying on the floor in one of the upstairs rooms. A cold, damp draft curls around the baseboards and flows across the floor. I try to remember when I last took my boots off. It's been days. I wonder if I still have a clean pair of socks. I doze for a while and then wake up to see a Verey shell explode in the sky outside the window. I glance at Doug and see that he too is awake.

"Is she nice?" he asks.

"Teresa?"

"Who else?"

"Yeah."

I wake again later to the sound of explosions in the streets nearby. I don't care. I roll over, close my eyes and go back to sleep.

Chapter 10

Christmas in Ortona

Saturday, December 25, 1943

"Get up! Get up *now*!"

The noise and shouting are sudden, loud and all around me. We're up before thinking, falling over one another, scrambling for our weapons.

"What the hell?"

Strong John is at the window with the Bren, Loon standing bleary-eyed beside him. Derrick, Doug and Specs are tumbling down the stairs. I tumble after them.

"The Jerries are breaking out!"

The Gaffer is leaning out of the doorway. I slip in beside him, prop my rifle against the door jamb and tighten my helmet strap under my chin.

"How the blazes . . . ?" says Doug. Like there should have been a warning.

A potato masher bounces against the outside wall and explodes.

Across the street, Turnbull's section is doing what we're doing, leaning into the street, shooting and yelling. I lean out too, past the Gaffer, in time to see half a dozen Paras running away. One stumbles and falls, gets up and falls down again, probably picked off by Strong John's Bren.

The enemy's hand-grenade sortie is over almost as soon as we wake up to it, but the sounds of battle are rising, not falling. Other weapons are being brought into action from windows up the street. Germans are returning fire from our end. The lieutenant jogs over from across the street with word that the Seaforths are fighting back against a major German counteroffensive launched from the cemetery.

He says, "Our visitors were part of that breakout. Only thing is, they advanced farther than they meant to. We almost cut them off."

But they attacked from the west side of town. "They came up *behind* us, from Dead Horse Square," I say.

"We're holding the square," says the Gaffer. "They *can't* have."

"You think they came all the way from the cemetery?"

He nods.

Lieutenant Gold is in touch with the company command post and the Gaffer is keeping close to the lieutenant. The two of them talk quietly in the kitchen. Meanwhile we sort ourselves out, check our weapons and supplies.

"Merry flippin' Christmas!" says Derrick suddenly.

Strong John grunts and Loon laughs bitterly.

"Hey, look!" says Derrick. "There's snow!"

It's not much of a snowfall. In fact, it looks a lot like freezing rain. But it throws a veil in the air, puts a shine on the street and a sheen on the rooftops.

The Gaffer emerges from his conference with the lieutenant. "Turnbull sent out a fighting patrol last night," he says. He tells us the next two houses between us and the corner are empty. "The Germans demolished the corner house, probably to give them a clear field of fire across the intersection. Same thing across the street. We're pretty sure there's a machine-gun nest around that corner, maybe one on each side. The fallen-down buildings are another barrier. When we get to it we'll come under a crossfire." He pauses and then adds, "Cheer up, boys! This will be a fun-packed day."

"What are the chances they'll come up behind us again?" I ask. "Like they did just now?"

"The Seaforths have our flank sealed but, just to be sure, the lieutenant is holding back Chudleigh's section. They've got our backsides covered."

"Can we bring up a couple of tanks?"

"No," says the Gaffer.

"Aw," says Loon.

"Not to worry. We're bringing up a gun. The arty chaps have been trying out different tactics. And we've still got the sappers."

We move out of the café at 0800 hours. With Turnbull's section on the other side of the street, we slip into the first house we come to. The Gaffer inspects the premises for hidden surprises. He finds one: it's just a trip wire tied across a doorway.

"Huh," says the Gaffer. "Amateurs!"

Sometimes the Germans set an obvious trap as a kind of decoy so we won't go looking for another bigger trap that's better concealed. Not this time.

We bring in the sappers to blow a hole in the wall leading into the next house. "There's a chance the Jerries have weapons trained on the street," says the lieutenant. "If we go through the wall, we're less likely to take casualties. I'd rather use up explosives than men."

Steve and Billy are looking weary. Billy is bent over by the weight of his backpack. I wonder if it's going without sleep that makes him look so tired, or knowing what he's carrying. Whatever Billy's feelings, the two of them go about their work efficiently. They blow open a hole and we pile through.

The Gaffer's tour of the building yields another clumsy booby trap. He can scarcely hide his disdain.

"One day, we'll have to set our own traps," I say. "Show them how it's done."

The Gaffer says nothing but looks interested.

"Give them back some of their own medicine," says Loon.

At about 0900 hours the 6-pounder is set up behind us and starts blasting away at a pile of rubble that is all that's left of the corner houses. Shots are fired in our direction from a rooftop. The lieutenant orders the sappers to punch a hole in the next outside wall, the one that connects us to the demolished corner house. His idea is to give Strong John a window for the Bren. If our calculations are accurate, the window will place him across from the German machine gun. The plan, as Strong John says, has its downside.

"I'm not complaining," he says. "But a German Mauser 42, against a Bren . . . "

The lieutenant nods his head sympathetically. "We'll give them something else to worry about," he says. "Let me see what we can come up with."

That one gun on our narrow street makes a heck of a noise as it bangs away at the rubble. Shrapnel and stone chips ricochet in all directions. To judge by the sound, the battle in the streets north of us is just as intense. The pop-and-bang of mortars, the rattle of machine guns and the more distant rumble of heavy artillery continue without let-up through the morning.

The sappers blow a hole where the lieutenant asked them to. It's about 3 feet above floor level, big enough to give a shooter a 90-degree view of the street, and yet narrow enough to make a difficult target. Or so we think.

"It's good," says Strong John. "A good job."

Even as he speaks, heavy-calibre bullets crack and splinters the edges of the hole.

"I guess the Jerries think it can be improved," says Loon.

* * *

The Gaffer's sitting on the top step of the staircase, looking thoughtfully at the hole on the other side of the room and the patch of grey sky beyond it. He's thinking out loud, weighing the options.

"We can't move the 6-pounder within range of the Jerries' machine gun," he says. The gun is quiet now, having blown away the rubble and whatever weapons or men the Germans had hidden behind it. The Gaffer keeps talking. "The street's too narrow for tanks to manoeuvre in. And if Strong John tries to set up in that hole, he's a goner.

"The lieutenant wants us to move ahead cautiously — avoid actions that put our lives at risk.

Which is all very well, but at the moment we're stuck."

I say nothing.

"What we need," says the Gaffer after a pause, "is a PIAT and a 2-inch mortar."

"What?" says Loon.

But the Gaffer has pulled his beanpole frame upright and is starting down the stairs. I have no idea what he means to do with a dodgy anti-tank weapon like a PIAT. The American bazooka is so much more reliable. We watch as he trots downstairs and then disappears.

"What's he up to?" asks Derrick.

I have no clue.

We wait. The house is damaged, but there are pictures on the wall, formal portraits of men with moustaches and hats, and black-haired women in long black dresses. There's a crucifix by the front door. It's weird that some things aren't damaged when others are completely destroyed.

The Gaffer returns after half an hour with a PIAT in his hands, and two men with a mortar. They looked cheerful.

"We need smoke," says the Gaffer.

"We're sending someone out there?"

"We're sending me," he says.

Our time of standing around comes to an end.

Strong John and Loon haul the Bren upstairs with instructions to start shooting at the Germans when the Germans starts shooting at the Gaffer. We roll out smoke and the Gaffer steps into it. He has the PIAT in his hands and a couple of armour-piercing shells in a bag slung over his shoulder. He's headed to the wrecked house next door, where he reckons there's enough of a wall still standing to give him somewhere to hide. The mortar crew hangs back.

The machine gun across the way starts shooting into the smoke and the Bren guns on our side promptly answer. A minute later we hear the peculiar *SHEBANG!* of the PIAT being fired, and the explosion when it finds its target. We throw out more smoke for the mortar crew as they dash out to join the Gaffer.

"By gosh, he's killed the Mauser!" says Derrick.

It's true that the German machine gun has gone quiet — for a moment — but then it starts up again. The Gaffer launches another missile. The Mauser keeps trying to find him while the Brens continue to seek out the gun.

We hear the bang of the mortar once, twice and then a third time.

Doug has been leaning out the door, peering around the corner, trying to see what's happening.

Now he slips outside, sticking to the wall, Sten gun at the ready. Derrick and I are close behind him. The smoke is thinning out. The German machine gun is silent.

I glance across the street. Turnbull's section is strung out like we are. They start jogging towards their corner.

"Now!" yells Doug.

We make a dash for it, round the corner on our side, in front of the Gaffer, and make a beeline for the building the Germans have been shooting from. A hole has been blasted in the outside wall by the PIAT. Black smoke streams out of the window that framed the Mauser nest. A Para, potato masher in hand, appears in the downstairs doorway. Doug opens fire as the German swings back his arm. He falls before he can throw the bomb and it explodes behind him, the force of the blast lifting and tossing him forward. I dodge him as he collapses. Doug, in front of me, disappears inside the building.

The front room is scarred, battered and empty. A voice beckons us from the back, shouting, *"Kamerad! Kamerad!"* and a single Para emerges with his hands above his head. I motion him outside and follow Doug and Derrick deeper into the building and up the stairs. We pile into the upstairs front room.

"Jeez," says Doug.

The room is a ruin, scarred and covered in soot. I prod the machine gun, now bent and broken, and it topples over. The bodies of the two men who had operated it are torn, twisted and disfigured.

The Gaffer comes upstairs behind us. "Their own mothers wouldn't know them," he says.

"What the heck, sergeant," I say. "Was that your idea, the PIAT and the mortar?"

"Well, son," he answers, "strictly speaking, it wasn't."

"Then what?"

"They were talking about it at company CP," he says. "Using the PIAT to pierce the wall and then using the mortar to frag the inside."

"Worked good," says Doug.

The Gaffer nods. He looks content.

* * *

We have a German cornered in an alley. He has a pile of sandbags in front of him, a dead comrade at his side, and the exit is sealed to his rear. Doug and I watch from across the street. He's an awkward target, helmeted and sitting low. He's using his own rifle methodically, picking his targets, taking his time. I hit him once, in the shoulder. He flicks at the wound contemptuously as if brushing off lint. Then, after propping up his weapon on a sandbag, he keeps on shooting with one hand. Another bullet grazes his cheek and blood floods down his chin. He barely pauses in his work.

Eventually, when his magazine is empty and he's slumping a little, he throws down his weapon. One of Turnbull's boys, Cadman, gets up, meaning to go in for the kill. The German just smiles. Cadman sees the smile, I guess, and takes it as a warning, because he stops in his tracks. The German rears back and throws a grenade at him. Cadman scuttles for cover and the duel goes on, the German tossing grenades one after another and somehow keeping from getting killed. He's struck by another bullet. We can see him recoil from the shock of the hit. His grin becomes a grimace. His face is a bloody mess. Somehow he arms and tosses another grenade in our direction. It must be his last. Cadman gets up again and the German, incredibly, reaches down and grabs a rock. Cadman has to duck as it flies past his head. The German goes down, finally, scrabbling blindly for something else to throw. Cadman stands over him, his weapon at the ready, but frozen, amazed by the German's insane determination.

"Surrender, you crazy fool," I hear him say.

The German looks up. Under the steel helmet, his face is streaked with blood, the skin beneath it drained of colour. He tries to speak but the sound he makes is a strangled moan. His eyes are filled with hate. There's no other way to describe them. And then the light behind them dims.

Cadman lowers his rifle. The German falls sideways and is still.

* * *

No matter how much explosive we use, Billy's backpack never gets lighter. Steve keeps sending him back to top up the supply.

"Can't be too careful," he says. "I don't want to be caught short."

I don't know what's going on between those two. Maybe they don't like each other. Or maybe Steve's a bully. You see that sometimes. The result is obvious: Billy, a little guy, finds it harder and harder to carry the load. The strain makes him slow.

He's slow to cross the street just short of the little square the lieutenant described to us, the one where several streets meet. A stream of machine-gun bullets chases and catches up with him as he scurries for cover. One hits his calf and his leg buckles under him. Another hits his lower back and he folds. A third hits his pack.

KABOOM!

There's a thunderous, fiery explosion and Billy is gone in cloud of light and smoke.

* * *

By the time we reach that little square, Piazza Plebiscito, the municipal square is securely in Edmonton hands. B Company is moving up the esplanade. Our company now holds the neighbourhood west of the Corso and, with the Seaforths on our left flank, we've penetrated parts of the old town. We are in contact with our comrades on every side and all elements are fully engaged. Our big guns are pounding the castle and its surroundings. We can call on tanks, 6-pounders and mortar crews when we need them.

The Germans aren't quitting. The harder we push, the harder they push back. Still, we're forcing them to give ground. We aren't at the end, but maybe the end is near.

We're holed up in a row of shops at the base of a hill. The remains of the cathedral loom above us. The Seaforths are around the corner. Rumour has it that the Germans have turned a flame-thrower against them. In any case, they're hunkered down beside us for a while. Now there's a duel going on between the enemy mortars and ours. Bombs are raining down on the street in waves. One of those waves brings Freddy Whitelaw and a handful of his Seaforths into our shop. They seem weirdly happy.

"Freddy, what's up?"

He grins and says, "Merry Christmas!"

There's no mistaking the change in him. There's a light in his eye and colour in his cheeks beneath the layer of dust and grime.

"You look like you mean it," I tell him.

"We've just come back from the church on the edge of town, San Costantinopoli. Or what's left of it."

"So now you're a churchgoer?"

"That's what the padre said. He said, 'Finally I've got you into church.' But we weren't there for the sermon."

"What then?"

"Christmas dinner."

"You're not serious!" It's 1700 hours and I haven't eaten since morning.

"Roast pork, Paul, hot from the oven, with crackling, gravy and apple sauce."

"You're killing me."

"Vegetables and stuffing," he says. "A bottle of beer for everyone."

"The beer that Monty promised us? It turned up at last?"

"Christmas pudding, Paul. Real Christmas pudding. There was fruit in it."

I groan.

"Lieutenant Gildersleeve played the organ and some of the men made up a choir. They sang carols."

"Christmas cake," I repeat.

Freddy looks at me pityingly. He reaches into his pocket. "I was saving this," he says. "But you can have it."

He hands me a tiny package wrapped in paper. I feel like a fool, but the sweet morsel inside the paper is more than I can resist. I take it, hesitate briefly, and tuck it inside my breast pocket.

"Thanks, Freddy," I say.

"See you around," he says.

"See you around."

* * *

"Dinner's on its way," says the Gaffer.

News of the Seaforths' feast has spread through the ranks. A few soldiers say that a dinner like that in the middle of battle is a mistake. It's sure to make men careless.

"Those guys all full of beer and good cheer," says Turnbull, "they're going to get killed."

The Gaffer nods his head in silent agreement, but he must know not everyone shares this view.

"I'd take the risk," says Loon.

Which is what I think too.

It's getting dark. The mortars have been quiet for a while. We've been told to expect some kind of night sortie by the Germans. The lieutenant has a plan to turn back any assault with a counter-attack of our own. The Saskatoon Light Infantry has set up machine guns to support us. Artillery will throw up illumination. It's hard to know what's squeezing our bellies — hunger or anticipation of a fight.

I'd hate to die now, when we've just about taken the town.

Another wave of mortar shells explodes in the square. The Germans are walking it from their end of town towards Via Cavour. Our side opens up and the square becomes a mass of noise, smoke and confusion.

"They're coming," says the Gaffer. "Wait for it."

Our section has been joined with Turnbull's. We gather at the door.

We hear the Germans before we see them. First come the grenades and then the spatter of automatic rifle fire. Then we hear shouts and footsteps.

"Wait!" says the Gaffer.

Glass shatters in the building next to us.

I hear Cadman suck in his breath. I tighten the grip on my rifle.

And then our heavy machine guns open up. The

effect is instantaneous. The Germans halt. The machine guns rattle on for a long moment as the Germans turn around. Then the guns cease too.

"Go!" shouts the Gaffer.

We pile out into the street. Verey lights explode in the sky above us. There are bodies on the ground and figures retreating towards the castle. We chase them in a ragged, open line, shooting erratically but exuberantly. The Gaffer sets the pace on the inside sidewalk nearest our row of shop fronts. We slow down as we reach the end of the square. The Gaffer has his arm up, signalling us to stop.

The surviving attackers have disappeared into the alleys that lead up to the cathedral and past it to the castle. In a moment we can expect their mortars to open up again.

"Far enough," says the Gaffer. He has a wounded German by the scruff of the neck and is dragging him back towards our shop beneath the hill. One of Turnbull's men is prodding another German before him. And then the barrage returns.

* * *

We get cold pork chops and cold fruit pudding. To be fair, the quartermaster's men took a risk in bringing it to us. We eat at our posts with our rifles in our laps. Later, I see a girl, she can't be more than nine, sitting in a doorway. She looks cold.

"Buon Natale," she says. *Merry Christmas.*

I keep walking. Suddenly I remember Freddy's gift, pause, turn and reach into my pocket for the quarter portion of paper-wrapped cake. She accepts it hesitantly.

"Buon Natale," I say. Merry Christmas.

Chapter 11

The Hostages

Sunday December 26, 1943

In the morning we move again.

"One more push," says the lieutenant. "The Jerries are still hanging onto the area around the cathedral. See these streets?" He points to his map and indicates the tangled passages between Piazza Municipale and Cathedrale San Tommaso. "Once we've driven them out, their only refuge is the castle."

The fighting is now in the north of the town. We — the Eddies — are getting close to the castle on one side, while the Seaforths are pressing the Germans on the other, western, side. In the streets and alleys in between, around and north of the cathedral, the Germans are still waging a determined, if hopeless battle. The Corso is ours and has been for a couple of days. Now that I can look down it from Piazza Municipale without having to duck and take cover, it's obvious that it's the town's main drag. It's where the best shops and main businesses are. Or were. We're standing around, waiting for orders, when Loon points at a wooden sign with a clock painted on it. It's hanging from a metal post above the burnt-out remains of a shop. Where once there were display cases, a counter, a work space, now there's only fire-blackened wreckage.

"Time's up," he says.

"That's sick," I say.

Strong John says, "Tell him to watch it."

"Okay," says Loon. "I *get* it."

Everywhere we look, there's rubble. At the far end of the Corso, a bulldozer is clearing a path so wheeled vehicles can get through. There are bodies too, not just of Germans, but also civilians. There's resistance still in the back streets. D Company has been mopping up, picking off snipers. Our sappers are blowing up mines. We seized and are holding the centre of town, but no one is relaxing yet. An enemy bullet can strike a man down at any time.

This is especially true on the northeast corner of Piazza Municipale. It's there, in the ground floor of an office building, that the lieutenant makes his command post.

"We're two sections now," he says. "The Gaffer will lead what remains of his own section plus Turnbull's. Chudleigh still leads the other one. We're working up these two blocks."

He's no longer pointing to the map. Instead, he gestures out the window.

"The little plaza up there is called Piazza Risorgimento. Our job is to clear out the two blocks below it. We'll be coordinating our movements with 8 Platoon, who are working the next street over, Via Matteotti. Between us, we're aiming to liberate the square in front of the cathedral. It's the last big square.

"Keep your heads up. These buildings are lousy with Jerries," he says and adds, "We can be pretty sure they're expecting us."

No doubt Lieutenant Gold is right and the enemy has his eye on us. But the grey stones and blank windows along the alley we're assigned to show no sign of life when Turnbull, hugging one wall, creeps slowly forward. Chudleigh's men, on the other side, put a Bren in place to cover him. A block away, the rest of the company is in some sort of firefight too.

We're crouched together on the corner, watching Turnbull's progress. When he's 10 or 12 feet up the street, Loon follows him, sticking to the same wall but keeping his distance. Turnbull stops in the shelter of a doorway. Loon stops too.

Turnbull glances back at the Gaffer, who nods, urging him on.

Turnbull reaches for the handle. I jog up behind Loon. The door opens, Turnbull steps back and a machine gun opens up.

BRRRCK! BRRRCK!

Turnbull is hit. His Sten gun strikes the street with a clatter. He's down, his right arm bleeding and broken.

Chudleigh's Bren blasts the windows beside and above the doorway. Loon and I scramble ahead, Loon with a 36 in his hand, armed and at the ready. He tosses the grenade through the open doorway. As soon as it explodes, I move up and fire two rounds into the interior.

There's no answering fire. When I peer inside, there's no enemy in sight. No dead Para, just a damaged reception area in a small office.

Loon and a couple of others are in the street helping Turnbull. He's on his feet, leaning on them heavily. I step inside the building. It might have been a lawyer's office. There's a couple of desks, a typewriter, a wooden filing cabinet. There's a vase on the counter containing dried flowers. Somehow, the blast of the grenade left it untouched.

The Gaffer appears beside me and begins his methodical search for booby traps. I stay close behind him, expecting the German to reappear.

It doesn't happen. We search the house — it

isn't booby-trapped. At the back we find an open door and a tiny courtyard. The German who had been there, waiting for us, must have climbed the wall to another courtyard.

The Gaffer calls me back. "You can bet he has that wall covered," he says.

I pull out a hand grenade. I look at him with a question in my eyes.

"Be my guest," he says.

I toss it; it explodes. Windows break, glass hits the ground, but no one screams. The enemy has moved on.

* * *

We take our time. The lieutenant plots each step. When we've secured the end of the alley, he calls up a Three Rivers Sherman to blast the front of a suspected German strongpoint. The tank is pulled back when the Germans answer with a shower of mortar shells. Then Chudleigh's section swings into action, taking another building, another casualty and a German prisoner.

The lieutenant knows how nearly worn out we are. He has the section leaders rotate men back between actions. The rear echelon has set up in Piazza Risorgimento, the little square between Municipale and the Esplanade, with tea and biscuits. An aid post has been established, not just for the wounded but also for men who have seen too much. One man, sitting alone, is weeping. I recognize another and call him by name.

"Shaun! It's me, Paul."

He stares straight ahead.

"Shaun?"

A medic, watching me, pipes up. "Forget it. He won't answer."

We're losing as many men to battle exhaustion as to the enemy. I wonder why I haven't been affected. What makes some men break?

I'm still in the square when the trucks arrive, half a dozen of them. There are ambulances too. The lieutenant sees them, sees me and motions me over.

He says, "It's for the people in the hospital."

"It's happening?"

He nods.

"I'm going," I say. He doesn't try to stop me. The lieutenant is tired too.

Doug sees me. He says, "What's up?"

"They're liberating the hostages."

I'm already running. He falls in behind me.

When you run through the streets, when you pay no attention to the tanks and the men with rifles in their hands, when you forgot about the enemy and the danger of snipers on rooftops, when you just run, knowing where you're going, not caring how heavy your pack is . . . you suddenly discover how small the town is. It's tiny. It's insignificant. And yet for this we and the Germans have been killing and maiming one another for a *week*! I run across the municipal square and down Via Cavour, past buildings that are half-destroyed, buildings we fought and killed for. Buildings that some of us died in. I run past officers who have questions in their eyes, who try half-heartedly to stop me. I'm not even sure what it is that's making me run. I only know I have to get to Dead Horse Square.

I slow to a walk when I get to the school. I round the corner, breathing heavily. A company of the Seaforth Highlanders has moved in. They have the hospital surrounded and are watching it warily.

"What's happening?" I ask the sergeant.

He gives me a look that says "Who the heck are you?" It's a look that sergeants learn in sergeant school. But then he shrugs and says, "They're coming out — the nuns, the patients, the people in the hospital. We've been told to hold our fire."

"Are the Jerries still in there?"

"They were sniping at us earlier. They've been quiet for a while."

"Have you seen a girl . . . ?"

I don't finish the sentence.

The hospital door swings open and two nuns appear, one after the other. The Seaforths grasp their weapons tighter and wait.

I look around the square, at the half-ruined church on the corner and the blasted school, at the wreckage between them and the bloated body of the horse. And then I see her, her shoulder-length black hair, her grey dress rippling in the breeze. She's approaching from the buildings on the far side of the square. I start walking towards her, then jogging. Doug is at my side.

The hostages emerge from the hospital singly and in pairs. Some are fully dressed. Others are wrapped in blankets and sheets. They're all thin. The strongest among them carry the weakest on stretchers. Those who are weak but can walk lean on canes or their friends. There are children too, clinging to their parents, or to the nursing sisters who bring up the rear.

We come together, Doug, Teresa and I, at the head of the wretched file. Sister Domenica sees me; her eyes flicker in recognition and she keeps on walking. Teresa nods too, but she has something else on her mind. She's moving against the flow of the patients.

Her sister!

Some of the Seaforths have closed in with us. They take over the handles of stretchers from some of the patients. They pick up stray children. The square is supernaturally quiet. Children cry. Mothers soothe them. The muffled sound of shoes on the pavement and the *clack* of crutches is all that can be heard in the cold air.

Four more figures emerge from the hospital. Four Paras step out, their coats open and their hands high above their heads. They walk down the steps behind the civilians. They take a few more strides and then stop. Some Seaforths start towards them when the near-silence is broken.

CRACK!

CRACK!

The shots are coming from the hospital. Two Germans go down, both struck in the back.

BRRRCK!

A Seaforth returns fire. An officer shouts, "Hold it!"

There are screams, curses, orders. Scores of voices making noise. The mass of people in the square surges forward. The two surviving Germans start to run. An officer calls out orders and a platoon moves up.

CRACK! CRACK!

More fire from the hospital. Incredibly, fanatical Germans inside the building are picking off the ones who surrendered. Another German goes down. More screams. More shouts. I dodge into the ragged crowd. Teresa is bent over a figure on a stretcher that has been dropped onto the ground. The child, Tomas, is crouched beside her. I peer past them and see Claudia's face, pale and bloody. Something — a bullet or shrapnel — has sliced into her neck. I kneel beside her.

Doug curses under his breath.

I glance at Teresa. Tears course down her cheeks.

The Germans are still shooting. Bullets are zipping past us, stone chips are flying up from under our feet. A section of Seaforths is herding the mass of civilians away from the field of fire. I don't wait. I rise up and run for the hospital door. Doug's hand is on my shoulder.

"Paul — "

I keep running. He follows me. I grab and swing open the hospital door.

* * *

I was an idiot to charge in like that. No one has to tell me.

Doug gets killed the moment we enter the hall. I feel rather than see him fall. I roll a hand grenade down the corridor. I hear screams when it explodes. A moment later the Seaforths are running past me. The sergeant I spoke to earlier stops briefly at my side. He looks at Doug and he looks at me.

He hisses at me, "What in *blazes* were you thinking?"

I can't say.

Why did Doug follow me? Why did *he* die instead of me?

* * *

I find Teresa later in Piazza Risorgimento, off Piazza Municipale, where the trucks and ambulances are waiting. Tomas is beside her. There's a sort of reception committee here, handing out food to the hungry and tending to those who are injured or sick. Teresa has a mug of tea in her hands, but she hasn't sipped from it. I sit down at her side.

"Where's Claudia?"

She turns her head and I see the bodies laid out in neat rows beside a wall. I put an arm around her shoulders. She rests her head under my chin. She's shivering. Cold.

"Cosa farai?" I ask her. *What will you do?*

"Cosa posso fare?" she says. *What can I do?* Then she says she will stay here, in Ortona.

"How will you live?"

"We have the land. And family."

"You have people you can stay with?"

"Not everyone is dead."

I stay with her a while longer. Someone gives us a blanket and Tomas falls asleep wrapped in the blanket in her arms. But then the quartermaster's crew starts herding people into the vehicles. The first of the ambulances starts up and drives away. A lieutenant is saying, "Come along now! Let's get moving!" Teresa stirs and I help her to her feet.

"Sono cosi' stanca," she says. *I'm so tired.*

But then she straightens up. She picks up Tomas and looks at me. I don't want to say goodbye. I guess she doesn't want to, either. We look at one another. I reach out and touch her cheek.

"Maybe someday . . . " I say.

"Si," she says. When this is over.

More engines start up, officers shout orders and in the background the sounds of war echo through the town. Tomas watches me solemnly over Teresa's shoulder as she walks away.

* * *

I feel numb as I make my way back to the Piazza Municipale. The inside of my head has gone dark. I can't think straight. I scarcely understand what I'm seeing.

The town is ruined. The remains of houses are heaped like stone corpses in the streets. Bits and pieces of people's lives are scattered among them. An upturned table, a torn book, a copper pot . . . random items that once meant something, but now are garbage. It seems to me that this is the end of everything.

Somehow I find my way back to the platoon. The Gaffer is bent over maps, talking to Lieutenant Gold. He sees me, says a word to the lieutenant and then strides towards me.

I say, "Doug's dead."

He says, "I know." He looks at me and says, "Are you okay?"

"Sergeant?"

"Are you hurt?"

"No."

He puts his hands on my shoulders, holds my gaze for a moment and then gives me a shake.

"Are you all there, Paul?" he says. "Do I need to send you back to the aid post?"

"No, sir."

"Are you sure?"

I'm not sure, but Specs brews tea and I sip some.

Strong John, cleaning his Bren gun, shakes his head sadly. Derrick is seated in a corner, leaning heavily against the wall. He has hardly spoken since Paddy was carried away. His eyes are closed.

I look at this handful of men and think, *This is all of us. All who came through Ortona.*

The Gaffer is watching me. He says, "It's not over yet. You know that?"

It takes me a moment to think about this. Finally, I laugh, sort of. "No," I say. "I guess not."

* * *

If any of us thought it was over, the enemy soon sets us straight.

8 Platoon, working its way up Matteotti, chases a bunch of Paras out of some kind of workshop or warehouse. The whole platoon — twenty-four men — piles into the building. Minutes later, it explodes.

The shock wave, the smoke and the dust blow our way. Even Strong John, who is bothered by nothing, looks up and says, "What was that?" God only knows how much explosive the Germans planted there. They're devils when it comes to demolition. Our boys are buried. Everyone is killed.

Or almost everyone. A work crew moves in immediately. They throw themselves into the work, tugging aside timbers and pushing away rubble, with shovels and their bare hands. And even while they work to save the buried soldiers, the Germans toss potato mashers at them.

Bastards.

Loon says, "We have to pay them back," which sounds like something you might hear on a playground, not a battlefield, but it's what all of us are thinking. Lieutenant Gold, grim-faced, consults Captain Trehan, while Chudleigh's section moves to push the Germans back from the wrecked building. When the lieutenant comes back with a pair of sappers, he and the Gaffer put their heads together to plot the next move.

Meanwhile, we keep moving towards the cathedral square.

We're all furious, but Loon, especially, is red-faced with rage. At every step, he is out in front of the rest of us. He shinnies up drainpipes and squirms through mouse holes. He crawls across rooftops and slides into attics. It's all we can do to keep up.

It's mid-afternoon when he disappears. We're in another smoking, roofless ruin. The Gaffer is looking at us, counting heads. Before he asks the question we're all thinking, Loon reappears.

"There's Jerries in the next house," he says. "Lots of them. An officer was shouting. I heard others moving around."

"Where were you?"

"There's a basement."

Loon shows the way and the sappers go to work. Somehow they plant explosives under the floor the Germans are standing on while the rest of us in 7 Platoon do everything we can to distract the enemy and keep them pinned down. The captain is on hand when the building goes up. The sappers must have planted high explosive by the bagful because the noise when it explodes is tremendous. The dust carries for blocks, and the building, when the smoke clears, looks like something a giant squashed. We lost twenty-three men on Matteotti. Just one was saved. Loon's revenge took at least as many Germans. The Gaffer is pleased.

* * *

On Monday we clear the square in front of what was left of the cathedral. By evening, the Eddies and the Seaforths are within yards of the cemetery and the castle. The next morning, when we wake up, the streets are quiet. The enemy has pulled out.

I run into Freddy on Tuesday. He says headquarters is crawling with reporters. The newspapers back home are calling the battle of Ortona "Little Stalingrad" after the siege of the Russian city last winter. Stalingrad was a lot bigger than Ortona, but I doubt if the fighting was fiercer. The mystery, says Freddy, is why the Germans fought so hard to hold it.

"Stalingrad was a big deal and everyone knew it," says Freddy. "When the Jerries lost Stalingrad, they lost Russia. But Ortona?"

"It's not like it's Rome," I say. "You could see why they would fight for the capital."

"The port's a small one. And anyway, they destroyed it."

"Maybe they couldn't bear the thought of losing. Maybe they thought they couldn't lose."

"I guess we showed them."

But did they lose? I'm not sure.

* * *

We get word before we move out that Paddy died. Derrick just nods his head when he's told the news.

"I saw him on the night he died," he tells me later. "You could call it a dream if you like, but I don't think it was a dream. He came to see me before he crossed over. He said not to worry. He was okay."

We buried Doug. Padre conducted the service. He spoke of Paddy, Jimmy and some of the others who lost their lives. He said they were brave, good-hearted young men who gave up their lives for their country. I would have said they gave everything they could to stay alive. Their lives were taken from them . . . but I suppose it makes no difference. They're not with us now.

I miss Doug. I'm surprised how much.

We have taken in new recruits. Loon has been promoted to corporal. Things change fast in this man's army.

I start on the letter the night before we pull out. I think of Doug's father, who already has lost his wife.

Dear Mr. MacDonald,

I was with Doug when he died. He was my friend and a brave soldier . . .

Dammit, this is hard.

Historical Note

By late 1943, Hitler's Germany was on the defensive. It had failed to conquer Britain, had lost the initiative in the Battle of the Atlantic, and was engaged in a desperate, losing battle on the Russian front. The Allied High Command was planning Operation Overlord, the landing in Normandy that, beginning in June 1944, would mark the beginning of the main thrust by the Western Allies through France and Belgium into Germany. Against this background, the Italian campaign was a sideshow. It was a distraction intended to force the Germans to take significant forces away from Northern Europe. For those who fought in Italy, however, this "sideshow" was a terrible, bloody campaign.

In December 1943, the First Canadian Division was part of the British Eighth Army, commanded by General Montgomery. While the United States Fifth Army was fighting its way up the western side of Italy, the Eighth Army was on the eastern, Adriatic side. Monty's strategy was to push past the port of Ortona to Pescara and then swing west along the Pescara road in a pincer movement with the Americans, aimed at the liberation of Rome. He planned to use Ortona as a port and winter base.

Two factors undermined Monty's strategy: the weather and the Germans. The weather should not have been a surprise. Italy in December was, as usual, cold and wet. The rivers from the mountains were swollen and the earth turned easily to mud. Allied air superiority was nullified by cloud cover and tanks were frequently stopped in their tracks. The strength of German resistance was less predictable. But Hitler, at this stage of the war, was micromanaging his generals, and the order to hold Ortona came from him.

It has been suggested by some that the Allies could have avoided the battle, bypassing the town and cutting off the German supply line to the north. In fact, while the 2nd Brigade of the Canadian 1st Division (including the Loyal Edmonton Regiment and the Seaforth Highlanders of Canada, with the Princess Patricia's Light Infantry in reserve) assaulted the town directly, the 1st Brigade (made up of the 48th Highlanders, the Royal Canadian Regiment and the Hastings and Prince Edward Regiment, the latter known as the Hasty

P's) moved up their left flank with the intention of encircling the town. What the division commander Major-General Chris Vokes did not (and could not) anticipate was the determination with which the Germans reinforced their defensive positions — bringing in elite, battle-hardened troops — and the ferocity with which they fought.

Ortona was a vicious battle, one that the Germans expected to win. When they lost, they believed at the time it was because they were outnumbered. They weren't. The record shows that the two sides were numerically nearly equally matched. The Canadians demonstrated in the streets of Ortona, as they had demonstrated before and would demonstrate again, that they were hardy, determined and, when necessary, ingenious soldiers, as good as any in the world. The Loyal Edmonton Regiment and Seaforth Highlanders of Canada between them lost 104 men killed, as well as 171 men wounded in Ortona's streets. The toll in December for all Canadian units was 1,837 wounded or sick and 502 killed. The Germans also paid a heavy price — and so did the local population. In a town of some 15,000 people in 1943, 1,314 civilians are said to have died.

The Italian campaign is overshadowed by the tremendous achievement of the D-Day landings, and the arduous drive to victory that ended with the death of Hitler and Germany's collapse. But Italy was a tremendous test for the men who endured it. Great feats were accomplished there and many tragedies unfolded. And Ortona still bears the scars.

The strain of fighting between the Moro River and Ortona is obvious in the faces of the Loyal Edmonton riflemen.

A company of the Seaforth Highlanders of Canada makes its way along the coastal path towards Ortona.

German demolition teams destroyed the cathedral of St. Thomas before the Canadians were close to the square where it is situated.

Riflemen from the Loyal Edmontons, supported by Sherman tanks of the Three Rivers Regiment, in Ortona two days before Christmas, 1943.

A Sherman tank of the Three Rivers Regiment advances down Corso Vittorio Emanuele in Ortona, December 23, 1943.

Brigade headquarters staff enjoy Christmas dinner, December 25, 1943, at San Vito Chietino, a couple of kilometres behind the lines.

The radioman had a heavy load to carry. Worse, he was often the first to be targeted by enemy snipers.

Just one man survived the booby trap on Via Matteotti: Lance-Corporal Roy Boyd of the Edmontons.

Boyd was buried in the rubble for thee and a half days before he was dug out and a stretcher crew could carry him back to the aid post.

The townspeople start life again in January 1943 amid the ruins of their town.

Two months after Ortona was taken, the Canadians continued the fight north of the town. Members of the Royal Canadian Artillery emerge from their dugout.

As winter of 1943 approached, the Allies moved in on Rome as the German army tried to slow the Allied advance.

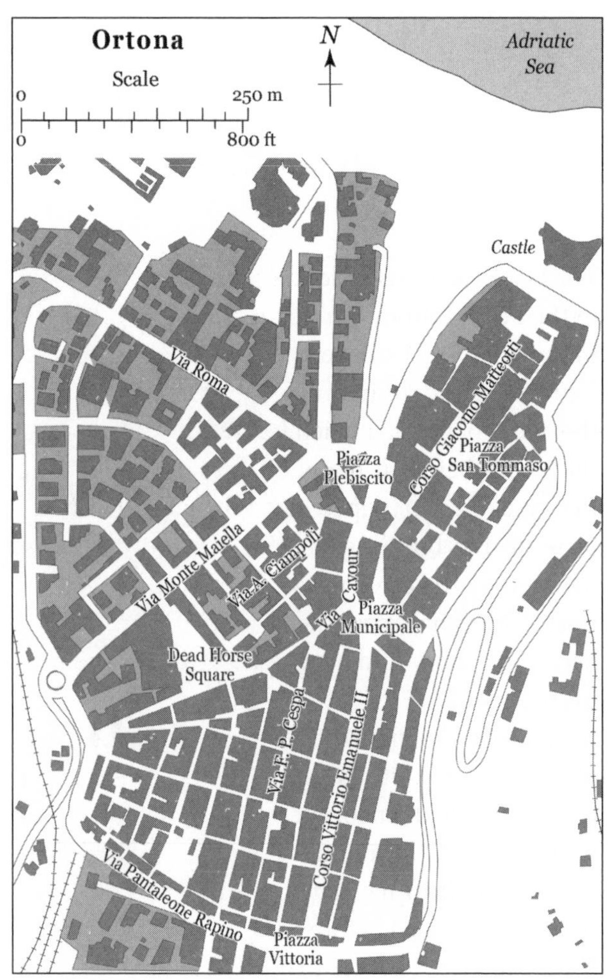

The port town of Ortona became the focal point for intense fighting along its narrow streets.

Author's Note

The father of a close friend of mine was a sergeant in the Loyal Edmonton Regiment. Like the Gaffer in the story, he had developed an uncanny instinct for finding and disarming booby traps. He missed the battle of Ortona when he was invalided out in the weeks before it happened. It was his platoon that was all but wiped out when the Germans blew up the building on Via Matteotti. He was haunted by the atrocity for the rest of his life. He was at least half-convinced that, if only he had been there, he would have sensed trouble and held his men back.

His story intrigued me, as did other aspects of the battle. Ortona was unlike anything the Canadians had encountered. It was fought in narrow streets in a small town that would have been difficult to navigate even if it had not been so badly damaged before the Canadians got there. It was intense. The enemy settled in as if it meant to stay no matter what the cost. It was impossible for the Canadians to employ air power, heavy artillery, or even mortars as they were accustomed to doing. Tanks were rendered particularly vulnerable because of the confined space and German defensive preparations. Small Canadian units — companies, platoons, even sections — found themselves on their own, their officers and NCOs having to invent new ways to push forward. They came up with mouse-holing and new uses for the much-despised PIAT, among other things. Their courage and sheer grit played a role too.

I was intrigued by the presence among the Eddies of a handful of men of Italian heritage. I wondered how it must have felt for them to fight in Italy. Those who remained at home, even if their families had lived in Canada for generations, were regarded with suspicion by their neighbours. The Royal Canadian Mounted Police compiled lists of Italian-Canadians (along with men and women of German, Japanese and Austrian heritage, all nations that were joined in the Axis alliance) who were suspected, often on flimsy evidence, of having fascist sympathies. Twenty-six camps were set up across the country to intern the suspected traitors. Italian-Canadians were held in three of them: in Kananaskis, Alberta; Petawawa, Ontario; and Halifax, Nova Scotia. Altogether, some six hundred Italian-Canadian men — and a handful of women — were imprisoned. The conditions in which they were kept were primitive. They lost not only their freedom but, in many cases, their businesses and possessions as well.

Paul's father, as I've portrayed him in my story, was more fortunate than many of the interned men. He was set free after a few months (there was an appeals process) and his family was able to keep his shop running while he was away. Even after his release he, along with thousands of others like him, would have been required to report every month to a government official, who was charged with keeping tabs on "enemy aliens."

Paul Baldassarra, of course, is an imagined character, as are the other members of his unit. Their push down Via Cespa is also imagined. It simplifies to a degree a series of encounters that are hard to track. The actual battle involved back and forth movements, with the Germans often slipping in behind Canadian positions, so that ground taken one day had to be retaken the next. The town, moreover, was so small, the streets going off at all angles, that the soldiers themselves had difficulty orienting themselves. An account by an Eddies lieutenant, for example, describes the fight for the school on Dead Horse Square as taking place on the Piazza Municipale. There is also an account of the Seaforths taking the same school. Different explanations for the confusion are possible. Noise, sleeplessness, the fog of war were likely factors. What is certain is that the troops sometimes hardly knew where they, or the enemy, were.

The major events described in the story are based on the record. Vokes, Hoffmeister, Jefferson and Stone were all participants in the action. Others, including Trehan and Gold, are fictional characters. Teresa and her sister are invented. However, an Italian woman did, in at least one instance, guide soldiers to their objective. More than one hundred civilians took refuge in the hospital and were led to safety by the nuns. Some German soldiers, more fanatical than others, were reported to have shot and killed those of their comrades who chose to surrender, a fact I used to embellish the hospital scene. I have tightened the narrative slightly: both the atrocity on Via Matteotti and the emergence of the civilians at the hospital occurred on December 27, not as in the story, on December 26.

I am indebted to Terry Copp, Professor Emeritus at Wilfrid Laurier University and Director of the Laurier Centre for Military and Strategic Disarmament Studies, who was generous in giving me access to the centre's resources and later in reviewing the manuscript. The primary documents he made available were invaluable. Among secondary sources, Mark Zuehlke's book, *Ortona: Canada's Epic World War II Battle* is essential reading. (It is from Zuehlke that the story of Major Stone's abortive charge down the Corso is drawn.) Saverio di Tullio's graphic history, *1943: The Road to Ortona* yields a surprising and authoritative Italian perspective. Marianna Tucci, at the Museo della Battaglia in Ortona, was not only an informative guide, but also a patient translator. She kindly introduced me to Tommaso Cespa, a survivor of the battle with vivid memories of the hardships he and his family endured. Thanks also to Lorenzo Apriani, my host during my stay in the town. My editor, Sandy Bogart Johnston, performed surgery on the manuscript with a deft hand. Freelance editor and fact-checker Janice Weaver conducted a detailed forensic exam on the remains. To the staff at Scholastic Canada Ltd., starting with my publisher, Diane Kerner, my thanks. Any errors that somehow got through despite their collective efforts are, of course, on me alone.

* * *

Jonathan Webb is the author of three previous books for young readers: *What's a Zoo Do?,* Red

Maple Award nominee *Journey to Mars: Quest for the Red Planet*, and White Pine and Hackmatack Awards nominee *Canada's Wars: An Illustrated History*. He has also written both fiction and non-fiction books for adults: his novel *Pluck* was co-winner of the Seal First Novel Award. Jonathan lives in Guelph, Ontario.

Credits

Cover cameo: Mr. Maurice Guerin, by permission of The Memory Project/Historica Canada.
Cover scene: *Platoon Commander Lieutenant I. Macdonald (with binoculars) ready to give order to attack at S. Leonardo di Ortona, Italy, 10 December 1943*; Lieut. Frederick G. Whitcombe, Canada, Dept. of National Defence, Library and Archives Canada PA-163411.
Cover details: journal vintage grungy yellow book cover © Dreamstime 55496615; set of grungy adhesive labels, price stickers, tags, free copy space © Shutterstock 27571093; grungy old paper with frayed edges © iStock Photo 3019095; belly band © ranplett/istockphoto; back cover label © Thomas Bethge/Shutterstock.
Page 217: *Personnel of The Loyal Edmonton Regiment during Street Fighting, San Leonardo di Ortona, Italy, 10 December 1943*; Credit: Canada. Dept. of National Defence, Library and Archives Canada PA-114487.
Page 218: *Men of B Company, Seaforth Highlanders of Canada, filing along mined coastal path. Town of Ortona in distance*; F.G. Whitcombe, Canada, Dept. of National Defence, Library and Archives Canada PA-152749.
Page 219: *Ruins of unidentified church* [possibly the cathedral of San Tommaso in Ortona]; Terry F. Rowe, Library and Archives Canada, Canada Dept. of National Defence PA-136308.
Page 220: *Infantry of the Edmonton Regiment supported by "Sherman" tanks of the Three Rivers Regiment, Ortona, Italy, 23 December 1943*; T.F. Rowe, Canada, Dept. of National Defence, Library and Archives Canada PA-114030.
Page 221: *"Sherman" tank of the Three Rivers Regiment, Ortona, Italy, 23 December 1943*; Canada, Dept. of National Defence,

Library and Archives Canada PA-114029.
Page 222: *General view of Brigade Headquarters at Christmas dinner*; Terry F. Rowe, Canada, Dept. of National Defence, Library and Archives Canada PA-152839.
Page 223: *Infantrymen of The Loyal Edmonton Regiment using a walkie-talkie radio during an advance, Ortona, Italy, 21 December 1943*; Terry F. Rowe, National Archives of Canada, MIKAN No. 3227873, PA-163932.
Page 224 (upper): *Infantrymen of The Loyal Edmonton Regiment rescuing Lance-Corporal Roy Boyd, who was trapped under rubble for 3 1/2 days, Ortona, Italy, 30 December 1943*; Lieut. Terry F. Rowe, Canada, Dept. of National Defence, Library and Archives Canada PA-152748.
Page 224 (lower): *Men of B Company, rescuing L. Cpl. Roy Boyd, Loyal Edmonton Reg...Ortona, 30 Dec., 1943*; Lieut. Terry F. Rowe, Canada. Dept. of National Defence, Library and Archives Canada MIKAN no. 4113916.
Page 225: *[Girl hanging out washing Ortona, Italy.]*; Terry F. Rowe, Department of National Defence, National Archives of Canada PA-114040.
Page 226: *Sergeant F.V. MacDougal and Sergeant-Major J.H. Ferguson, 2nd Field Regiment, Royal Canadian Artillery (R.C.A.), emerging from their dugout north of Ortona, Italy, 15 February 1944*; Lieut. Strathy E.E. Smith, Canada, Dept. of National Defence, Library and Archives Canada PA-193899.
Pages 227 and 228: Maps by Paul Heersink, Paperglyphs.